CW00829168

THE SPINNING MULE

The Spinning Mule

HAROLD CATLING
BSc(Eng), PhD, CEng, FIMechE, FTI

The Lancashire Library
1986

Published by Lancashire County Council
Library and Leisure Committee

Originally published by David & Charles, 1970

ISBN 0-902228-61-7

Printed by John Bentley (Printers) Ltd., Todmorden
A member of the Dunn & Wilson Group

Contents

Preface to the New Edition

It is now some twenty years since the collection of material for this book began. Even at that time relatively few mules remained in operation in the Lancashire textile industry. The intervening years have seen the virtual extinction of the machine. Indeed, not only has the mule given way, but also its successor the ring frame has now begun to give way to the new 'open end' spinning machines which will run virtually untended night and day.

However, the same period has seen a considerable growth of interest in the history of textile manufacture and there are now sites where mules can be seen in preservation and even in operation. Reference to some of these can be found towards the end of the book.

I am very pleased to see this new edition appear, as I believe that it will give visitors to our museums a broader understanding of the nature of both the machinery and the way of life which constituted the Lancashire textile industry during more than a century of world dominance.

HAROLD CATLING
July 1986.

Acknowledgements

I am particularly grateful to Mr G. B. Shipton who has drawn all of the many original figures used to illustrate the text. I am also grateful to Mary, my wife, who has spent many hours in the preparation of the typescript and to other members of my family who have taken a keen interest in the work and helped with advice and constructive criticism.

HAROLD CATLING

List of Illustrations

PLATES

Other plates and Figs 8, 9, 26, 27, 28 and 29 have been reproduced from various sources by Mr C. W. Bradley and Mr R. A. Barker

LIST OF ILLUSTRATIONS

FIGURES IN TEXT

Preface

THE mule, a machine combining the spinning action of the jenny with the drafting action of the water-frame, was invented by Samuel Crompton in the late eighteenth century. As a textile machine it was immediately and completely successful, so successful indeed that for the next hundred years it was subjected to intensive engineering development directed towards making it a completely automatic machine.

Crompton's original machine had only a dozen or so spindles and was both manually powered and manually controlled. Within a decade of its invention, however, a number of engineers, notably in Manchester and in Lanarkshire, were building mules with upwards of 100 spindles which could be driven by animal or water power. The earliest of these were entirely manually controlled: but strenuous efforts were made to automate each of the five separate processes or functions which constitute the mule spinning cycle. With four of the functions there was no serious difficulty and by 1800 the manually controlled, power driven mule had been developed to the form in which it continued to be used for more than sixty years.

In this form all functions except winding were completely automated. Many attempts to automate winding were made but without success until, in 1830, Richard Roberts invented his remarkably ingenious 'winding quadrant'. This device fulfilled the complex requirements of the situation so precisely, yet so simply, that it found immediate acceptance. From that date the construction of manually controlled mules virtually ceased and many of those already in existence were converted to 'self-actors' on the Roberts' principle.

The mule cycle of operations is repeated from three to five times per minute and in the early days it was regarded as sufficient that a self-actor should be able to perform just a few successive cycles without attention. After all, this was an enormous improvement on its predecessor which required a considerable measure of both skill and muscular effort during a substantial part of each spinning cycle, and it was not regarded as at all onerous that the spinner had to make progressive adjustments to the mechanism as winding proceeded from the bare spindle to the completed cop of yarn. Inevitably, however, the quest for complete automation continued. Various refinements were successively introduced until, by 1880, the self-acting mule was virtually perfect.

In its final form the mule became almost the universal spinning machine, able to spin the finest yarns and the coarsest, strong lean yarns or soft full yarns, more cheaply than was possible by any other means. Gradually, however, the ring frame, a continuous spinning machine, began to be preferred and practically no mules have been built since 1914. Today the amount of yarn spun on mules is a negligible fraction of the total. Like the crossbow, the stagecoach and the square-rigged clipper ship the spinning mule burst on an astonished world, had its brief hour of glory, and departed.

It is fascinating to look back to those days when the greatest export industry Britain has ever known was being built on the labours of an army of men and boys dedicated to obtaining the maximum amount of yarn from upwards of 40,000,000 spindles throughout every minute of a very long working week. The jenny gate was a truly exotic place. In the hot and humid conditions which mule spinning demanded all laboured barefoot and scantily clad. Each pair of mules was staffed by a small team intensely loyal to its leader, the minder, whose word was law in his little kingdom. In this atmosphere men grew together, forming closely knit communities in which they lived a life apart, as do miners and fishermen today.

Those days are gone. To future generations it may seem unbelievable that such a machine as the mule, with a carriage almost 150 ft long and carrying 1,300 spindles in a single row, could ever have been built. It will seem even less credible that in Lancashire alone there were once 50,000,000 such spindles, each accelerated to 10,000 revolutions per minute, before being stopped and reversed with infinite precision, four times a minute throughout a fifty-six hour week. Soon there will be only a few drastically shortened remnants of these machines standing lifeless in museums to remind us of what has been.

1

Spinning Before the Mule

ALTHOUGH no examples of his textiles survive, it is thought probable that palaeolithic man spun natural fibres into yarn. There is, however, no doubt that the spinning of flax was already a domestic art in Egypt 7,000 years ago. In other countries too, spinning has a long history. In India cotton was most widely used, the Chinese preferred hemp and silk, and in Babylonia and Assyria much woollen cloth was produced.

From those distant days until comparatively recent times the only way of spinning known was by means of the incredibly slow and tedious distaff and spindle. This method was so slow that it took a spinster, working steadily for twelve hours a day, upwards of sixty working days to spin only 1 oz of the fine yarns used in Indian muslins.

Despite the enormous amount of labour used in spinning, mechanization proceeded only slowly. The first step, the provision of a whorl or flywheel (usually of stone or baked clay) at the lower end of the spindle to facilitate rapid rotation was introduced independently in many parts of the world. Although crude, this continued to be used for many centuries and remains in limited use today. It was succeeded by a simple manually-rotated wheel arranged to drive a single spindle by means of a band passing round the spindle whorl. With the great wheel, as it came to be known, yarn could be spun more quickly: but there was an important disadvantage. With spindle and distaff one could spin while walking about, tending the sheep or visiting the market: but the wheel was far less portable and for this reason usually used at home. In many parts of this country it was known as 'the cottage wheel' because it was used at home and not carried by the spinster.

At this stage in the development of the art, spinning was still a rather tedious business. With the spindle of the cottage wheel rotating at a high speed, the spinster first drew out and twisted as long a length of yarn as she could conveniently manage—about 4 ft for the simple spindle and whorl, and perhaps 5 or 6 ft for the great wheel. The yarn was twisted by being attached to the rotating spindle and held at such an angle as to allow coils to slip continuously from the spindle tip in the way shown in Fig 1. When it was judged that a length (or draw) of yarn was sufficiently twisted the spindle was stopped, the few turns on the bare part of the spindle blade were unwound and then the new length of yarn was wound onto the cop of yarn already on the spindle.

Before resuming spinning the spindle was accelerated to full speed and the few inches of yarn from the preceding draw allowed to coil along the spindle blade from the cop to the tip. Then one hand was used to draw out more roving at such an angle that the last coil was able to slip easily from the spindle tip with each turn of the spindle. The other hand was used, as necessary, to keep the spindle turning. The turns slipping from the spindle tip quickly travelled along the yarn to twist, and thus form into yarn, the fibres issuing from between the finger and thumb of the spinster's drawing hand.

The speed with which yarn could be spun depended on the fineness of the yarn and the amount of twist needed: but, particularly with coarse, low-twist yarns, the frequent interruptions necessary for backing-off and winding greatly limited development of the process. It is probable therefore that men's thoughts were often directed towards means by which continuous spinning could be achieved. The earliest record of a continuous spinning device was made by Leonardo da Vinci who, in 1519, described a ∩-shaped 'flyer' and means for traversing the bobbin along the spindle so as to wind the yarn in uniform layers.

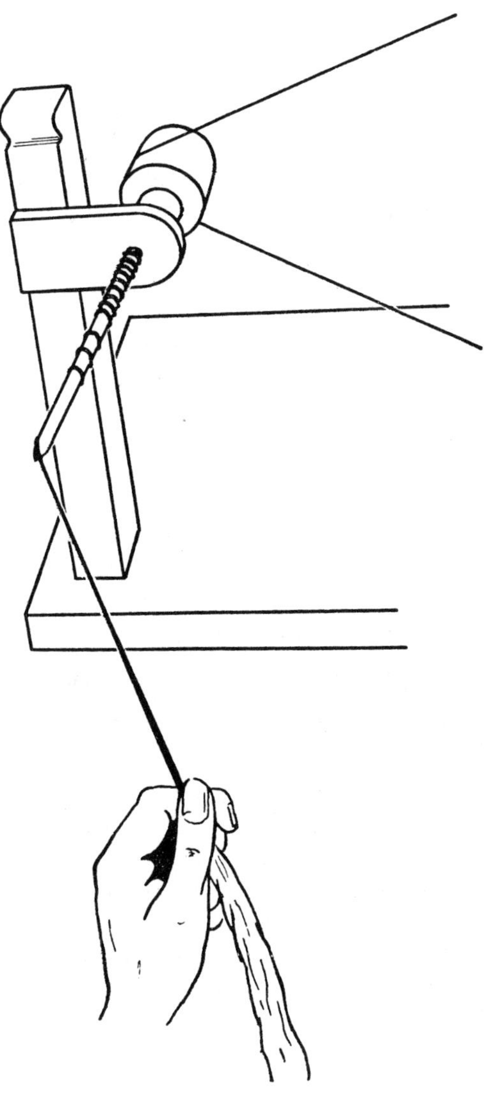

Fig 1. This is the principle used in the cottage wheel, the jenny and the mule

The invention of the flyer marked a big step forward, since for the first time it allowed the processes of twisting and winding to proceed simultaneously. In its simplest form the flyer is fixed to the rotating spindle, and the bobbin, which is free on the spindle, is dragged round by the yarn against the friction of a cord wrapped round a pulley forming part of the bobbin. Rotation of the assembly as a whole introduces twist. Relative rotation of flyer and bobbin causes the spun yarn to be wound onto the bobbin. In the simple form the tension is determined by a weight attached to the friction cord.

In the more highly developed form shown in Fig 2, the flyer, fixed to the spindle, is rotated at a higher speed than the bobbin, which runs freely on the spindle. Both flyer and bobbin are driven by the same band, which passes twice round the driving wheel and once round each of the whorls fixed to the spindle and the bobbin respectively. Because the tension maintained in the yarn during spinning is that needed to induce continuous slippage, or more properly 'creep', between the driving band and the whorls the tension in the driving band is critical. A facility for ready but sensitive adjustment of the band tension is always provided. Although da Vinci himself did not exploit the principle it was very quickly taken up in various parts of Europe. One embodiment of the principle, the Saxony wheel, appeared in 1555 and quickly became established as offering the most efficient way of spinning the relatively coarse woollen and linen yarns, which were then in such demand in Europe. It was a simple spindle and flyer without continuous traversing means: but, by arranging that the wheel was treadle-driven, it left the spinster with both hands free to manipulate the fibres. There can be no doubt that this simple device greatly increased the output of the spinsters. Adam Smith estimated that, for the types of yarn spun in Europe, productivity was doubled by the introduction of the Saxony wheel.

It seemed logical, therefore, that development should continue along the same lines. There seemed little to be said for a return to discontinuous methods of spinning. Many attempts were made to evolve a multiple-spindle machine based on Leonardo da Vinci's principle, but the greatest difficulty was experienced in finding

Page 17: (above) Spinning on a cottage wheel; (below) Spinning on a Saxony wheel. The spinner is Mr Patterson, curator of the Castle Museum, York

Page 18: (above) Hargreaves jenny, as reconstructed by TMM (Research) Ltd (now in the TMM Museum of Early Textile Machinery); (below) A jenny used until comparatively recently in Dobcross, Yorkshire (now in the Bankfield Museum, Halifax)

mechanical means for drawing out the roving to the required degree of fineness.

The idea of using drafting rollers, a succession of pairs of rollers, each pair running faster than the preceding pair, occurred to a number of people: but successful implementation of the idea took many years. Although drafting as practised today appears to be a very simple and straightforward process it is, in fact, an extremely complex technology, which is still the subject of a great deal of theoretical and experimental study. It was not until 1733 that John Wyatt, working at Sutton Coldfield in Warwickshire, achieved a degree of success sufficient to warrant his embarking on the construction of a small mill to spin cotton 'without the intervention of the human fingers'.

In partnership with Lewis Paul, who took out a patent 'for the spinning of wool and cotton in a manner entirely new' in 1738, Wyatt built his first mill at Birmingham in 1741. The patent clearly describes roller drafting as we now know it:

> As the prepared mass, rope, thread or sliver passes regularly through or betwixt these rowlers, cillinders or cones a succession of other rowlers, cillinders or cones, moving proportionately faster than the first, draws the rope, thread or sliver in any degree of fineness which may be required.

No claim is made for a novel method of twisting and it is reasonable to infer that at this date the well-established bobbin and flyer mechanism would be used as a matter of course.

This first mill, driven by two asses, was probably not completely successful for the machinery was sold after only two years. The confidence of the inventor and sponsors was not impaired. It may indeed, have been increased by their experience in Birmingham, for a larger, water-driven mill was established at Northampton in the same year. The new mill contained five spinning frames, each of fifty spindles, and each able to spin about ninety hanks of 15's count cotton yarn in a working day.[1] That labour difficulties limited production is indicated by a letter written in October 1743, in which

[1] One hank of cotton yarn contains 840 yd, and '15's count' implies that 15 hanks of that particular yarn weigh 1 lb.

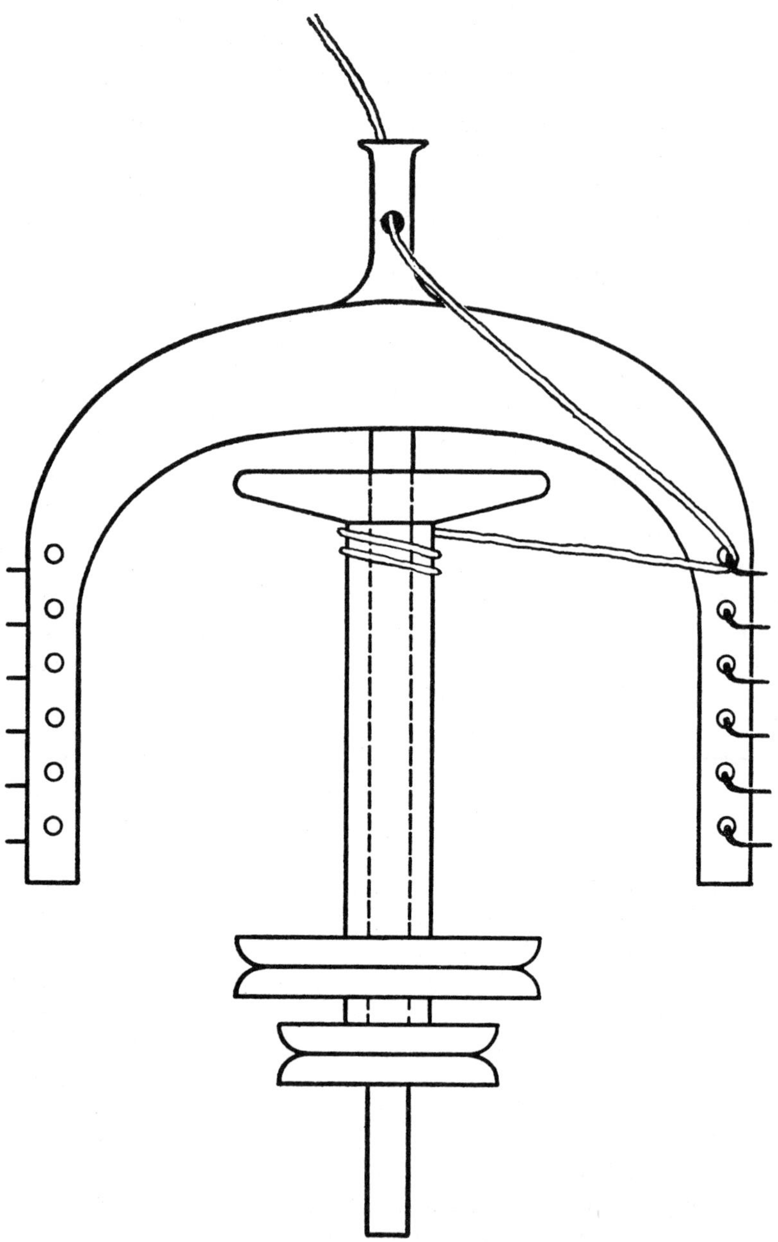

Fig 2. Continuous spinning with spindle and flyer. The basis of the Saxony wheel, Arkwright's 'Water Frame' and later throstles

Wyatt complained that they 'seldom had hands to keep four frames at work'.

A great deal of information concerning the Northampton mill is contained in *A Systematical Essay on the Business of Spinning* written by Wyatt in 1743. The assumption that twisting was by bobbin and flyer is supported by the statement that 'The bobbin revolved upon the spindle, and each was moved by a separate wheel and pinion, containing, the one sixty four teeth, and the other sixty five'. The whole cost of the plant is estimated at £3 per bobbin. Wyatt's *Essay* included some market research, mostly carried out in London, covering yarns from 12's at 1s 6d per lb to 80's at 20s 6d per lb. So far as the quality of fine yarns was concerned the imports by the East India Company, typified by their 60's at 14s per lb, were regarded as setting a high standard which the domestic product might approach but could scarcely hope to equal.

It is difficult to say just how successful the Northampton venture was. The mill continued to be used and was sold with the original machinery intact in 1764, but it was not so successful as to be copied widely by others during Wyatt's lifetime.

The essential principles of Wyatt's system of spinning were embodied in the 'Water Frame' patented by Richard Arkwright in 1769. The new machines, shown schematically in Fig 3, differed somewhat in detail from those used in the Birmingham mill: but there can be no doubt that they were based on the Wyatt and Paul designs. Arkwright, however, succeeded completely. He built new mills in Derbyshire, Lancashire and Scotland to meet the rapidly growing demand for fine cottons, and 'wealth flowed in upon him with a full stream'. Many mills were built under licence from Arkwright and even more were built in defiance of the patents. Within sixteen years of publication of the patent, more than £500,000 had been spent in Britain in the erection of mills using the water frame and upwards of 35,000 persons were employed in them.

The early difficulties posed by the complex technology of roller drafting had, however, encouraged other inventors to follow another avenue of development. Roller drafting is difficult because it is an inherently unstable process. For an assembly of fibres to be attenuated uniformly, it is necessary for the fibres to slip relative to one

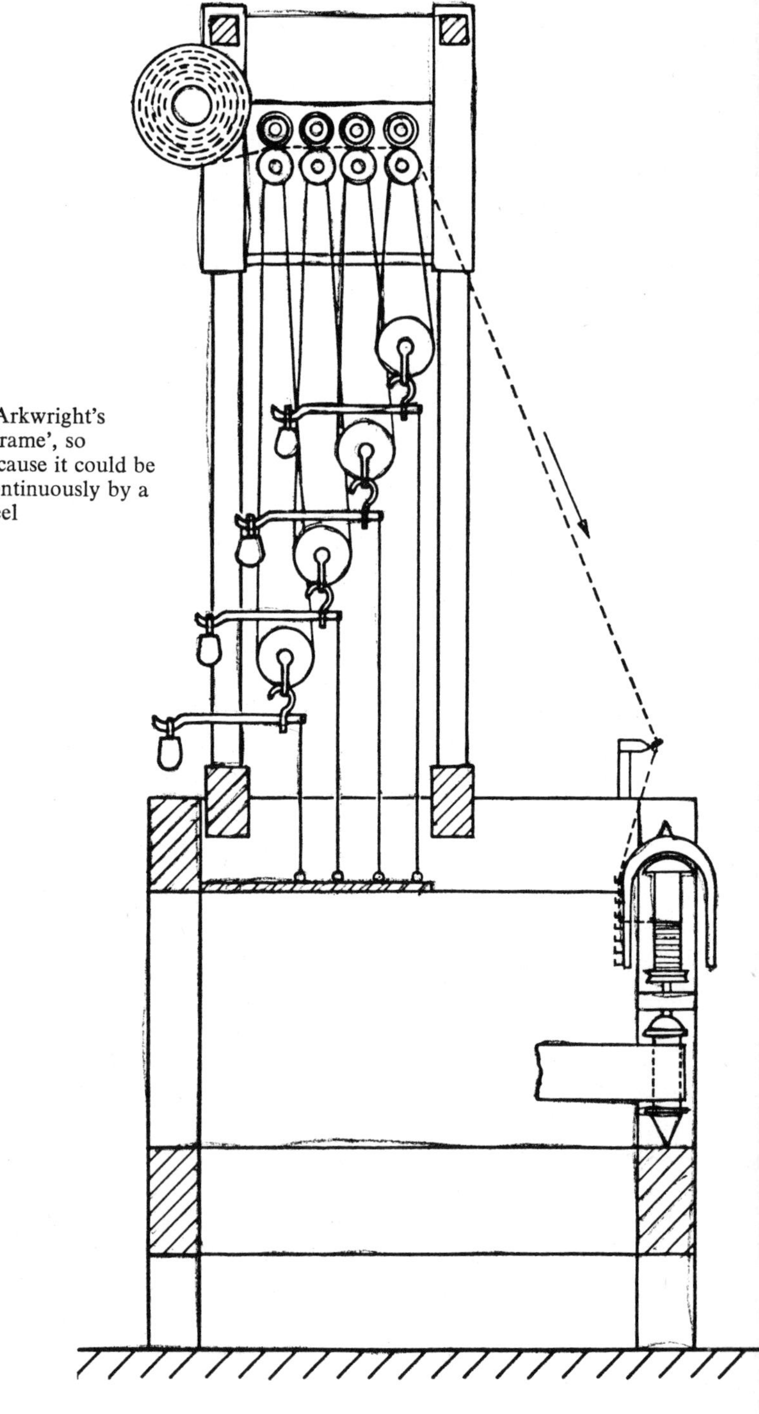

Fig 3. Arkwright's 'Water Frame', so called because it could be driven continuously by a waterwheel

another equally and readily along the whole length between the two points at which they are gripped. Unfortunately, the coefficient of friction between fibres is greatly reduced once sliding begins to occur. In consequence there is a strong tendency for the assembly to yield first at its thinnest place and, as drawing proceeds, for the thin places to become even thinner without the thick places being attenuated at all. In the hand-spinning processes, drafting takes place only after some twist has been introduced into the fibre assembly and the spinster continues introducing twist as drawing proceeds.

The working principle on which this method of drafting depends is that a lightly twisted length of roving is stable during axial extension. This results from the fact that the frictional cohesion between overlapping fibres at any point in the length is dependent on the degree of twist in the roving at that point and the fact that twist always tends to run into the thinnest parts of a roving or yarn. The relationship between twist and cohesion is not a simple one, but over a wide range of conditions it is such that the thin parts of a roving are actually stronger than the thick parts. Thus, when a draft is applied the thick parts yield first, and as drafting proceeds the roving tends to become progressively more uniform. Naturally, as the thick parts are reduced, twist tends to flow from the thin parts to strengthen the formerly thick parts and the whole process is conveniently stable.

The use of this principle is subject to one important limitation. For practical stability the relationship between the thickness of a roving and the degree of twist it contains must lie within particular limits. For any roving or yarn this relationship is specified by a single number, known as the twist factor, which is proportional to both the thickness of a yarn and the number of turns of twist in unit length of the yarn. When the twist factor is very high, cohesion between fibres is so great that they will break before sliding, but when the twist factor is too low there is not enough twist-induced cohesion sufficiently to strengthen the thin places.

In the English cotton count system a twist factor of 4 gives maximum strength to a typical cotton yarn and the yarn will break rather than draft. Really satisfactory drafting against twist is obtained only when the twist factor is in the range 2 to 3. As drafting proceeds the twist factor is, of course, reduced, for not only is the number of turns of twist per unit length reduced but also the thickness.

Consider what happens when we draw out a cotton roving which initially has a twist factor of 3. If the roving is extended by 50 per cent the number of turns per unit length is directly reduced in the proportion of 3 to 2. At the same time, the thickness is reduced in proportion to the square root of the increase in length, ie in the proportion

$$\sqrt{3} \text{ to } \sqrt{2}$$

Thus, the twist factor is reduced from

$$3 \text{ to } 2\,\frac{\sqrt{2}}{\sqrt{3}} \text{ ie from 3 to 1·633}$$

This is too high a degree of attenuation as it reduces the twist factor to a value below the minimum for stable drafting to take place.

Yarns made by drafting against twist have a distinctive character, a softness or fullness which makes them specially suitable for a number of end uses. Blankets, raised-cotton sheets and woollen (as distinct from worsted) suitings use yarns of this sort spun on the woollen or cotton condenser system. For many other purposes, where a strong, lean yarn is demanded, they cannot be used. Here drafts involving extension to the order of 400 to 4,000 per cent are needed in order to straighten and parallellise the fibres. Such high drafts, giving strong, highly oriented yarns, were easily obtained by using the primitive distaff and spindle and introducing twist progressively as attenuation proceeded. By this means the superb fine cottons of India were spun. It was, therefore, an attractive alternative to grappling with the problems of the distinctly refractory new technology of roller drafting to attempt mechanisation of the primitive process.

It is true that the discontinuous nature of the process led to many difficulties. They were, however, mostly of a type likely to yield to mechanical ingenuity, and the increasing demand for yarn in the early eighteenth century encouraged many to try their hand. Their attempts are only sparsely recorded, although the transactions of the Society for the Encouragement of Arts show the submission of at least six spinning machines as claimants for premiums to be awarded by the Society in the period 1761 to 1767.

By far the best-documented development was that of James Hargreaves' jenny, patented in 1770. Hargreaves was born at Oswaldtwistle in 1720 and continued to live and work in that part of Lancashire until local opposition to the introduction of his jenny caused him to leave the county and take his invention to Nottingham.

Although textile manufacture was still largely a cottage industry, the cotton trade in Lancashire had become a highly organised capitalist enterprise. The companies concerned were often quite large, finding employment for up to 5,000 people and undertaking the whole financial operation of importing cotton, paying the work people and marketing the cloth. A common arrangement was for the company to provide the weaver with cotton and pay him for the conversion when he later delivered the completed grey cloth. The weaver was free to make what arrangements he wished for the spinning of the yarn, subject only to his cloth being of a satisfactory quality and complying with the specification demanded by the company.

While Hargreaves was a young man the fly-shuttle, invented by Kay in 1733, became widely used and greatly increased the productivity of the loom. Previously it had been possible for the women of a family to keep the head of the household supplied with as much yarn as he could weave, but now the output of five or six spinsters was needed to keep one loom working. As a commission weaver Hargreaves was probably often held up for lack of yarn, and for this reason applied himself to the development of devices to expedite spinning. He had early success with improved methods of carding and went on to develop his jenny, probably in the late 1750s.

The jenny is no more than a mechanical contrivance by which one operator is able to carry out the operations of distaff and spindle spinning on a number of spindles at once. The working elements are shown in Fig 4. A creel of roving bobbins replaces the

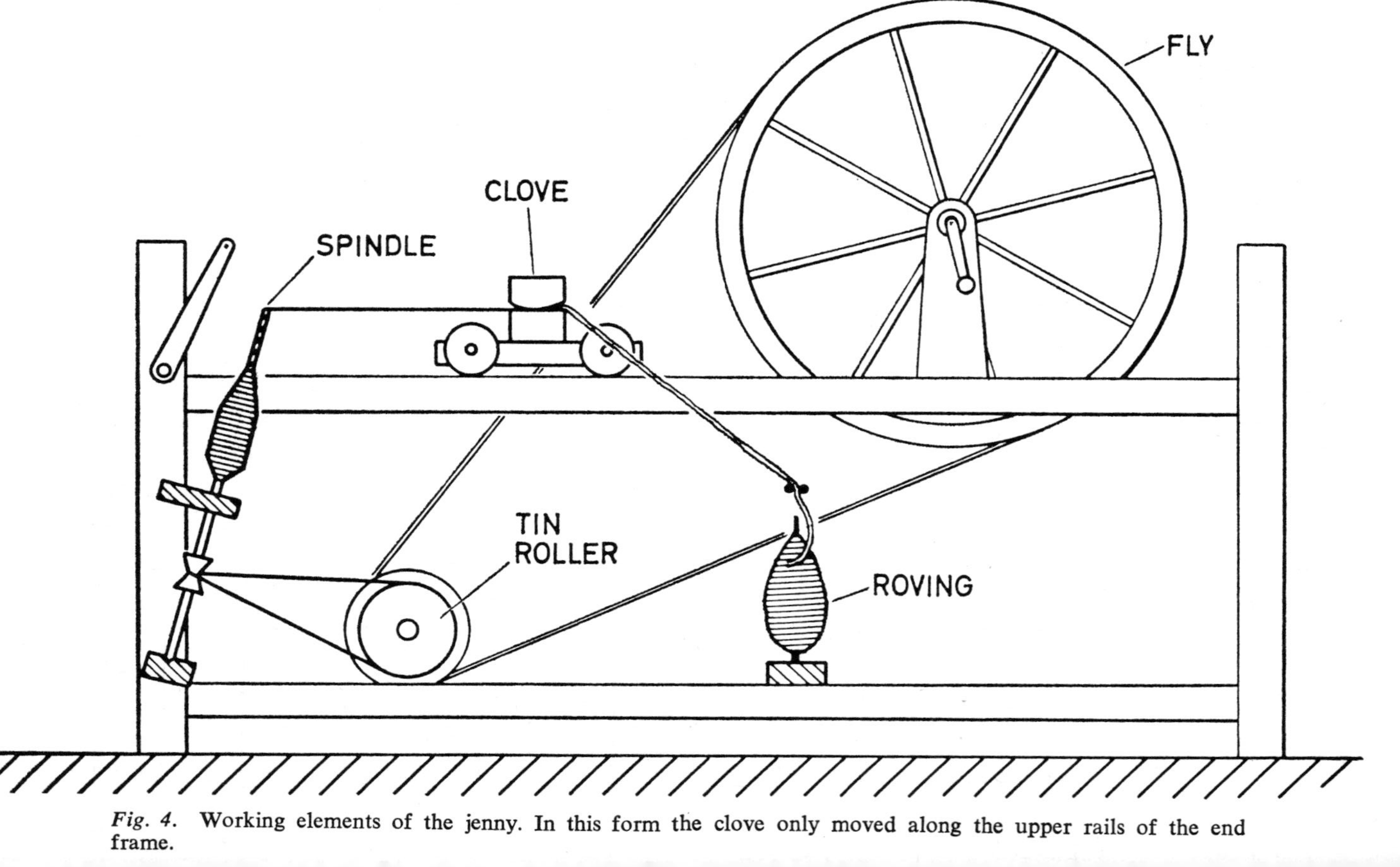

Fig. 4. Working elements of the jenny. In this form the clove only moved along the upper rails of the end frame.

distaff and a readily operated wooden clasp or clove is used to grip all the rovings simultaneously. The clove is carried on guides, so arranged that as it is drawn away from the spindles to attenuate the roving, it remains parallel to the row of spindles and draws out all rovings equally. The spindles are so disposed to the clove as to permit twist to run freely from the spindle tips without allowing the yarn itself to be withdrawn from the spindle. The spindles are driven via cords or bands from a common shaft, usually known as the swift, or fly.

Hargreaves made his first machine working alone with a pocket-knife as his principal tool. It had eight spindles, and the clasp, or clove, which gripped the rovings was simply a split briar stalk. Although crude there is no doubt that it was effective and during the next few years it was followed by successively larger machines. By 1766 a number of Hargreaves' relatives and friends in the Blackburn area were using the new machine for the spinning of weft. Its very success led to jealousy and fear of unemployment amongst those unwilling to accept change, and early in 1768 there was rioting in the area and many jennies were smashed. Shortly afterwards Hargreaves moved to Nottingham and continued to develop his invention, taking out a patent, rather belatedly, in 1770.

By this time the jenny was firmly established. Some machines had been built by Hargreaves himself but many more were free interpretations of the principles embodied in the original design. The fundamental principle was that of taking a number of short lengths of roving or slubbing and drawing them out steadily while continuing to introduce twist into them by rotation of a number of spindles driven from a common wheel. Hargreaves' first machine had eight spindles but no detailed description of the arrangement of the early machines survives. The patent specification of 1770, however, contains a very precise description—so precise that in 1964 members of the Helmshore Local History Society were able to construct a replica of the sixteen-spindle machine and carry out a detailed technical evaluation of its performance.

Although the disposition of the working elements was varied widely, all jennies used the same basic operating cycle. The succession of operations which make up the complete cycle of the process have much in common with both the primitive spindle and whorl process and the later cottage wheel process. It can conveniently be regarded as a five-operation cycle and in Fig 5 the working elements of a jenny are shown in the relative positions they occupy before and after each operation.

Regarding laying-on as the operation completing the preceding cycle, the first task in the new cycle is to release the clove and draw it away from the spindles, allowing a few inches of new roving to pass freely into the spinning zone. On securing the clove, preparation for drawing is completed, and a short length of yarn attached to a short length of soft roving is held between the spindle tip and the clove. Rotation of the spindles is now begun, and at the same time the clove is pulled steadily away from the spindles to draw out the roving into yarn. The art in this operation is to maintain the relationship between the rate of spindle rotation and the rate of withdrawal of the clove so that drafting proceeds smoothly, the thicker places always yielding before the thinner places, so that at the end of the draw the yarn is not only thinner but very much more uniform than the roving from which it has been made. (That this is possible is the outstanding quality of jenny spinning. With even the most highly developed forms of a simple roller drafting it is impossible to spin yarn more regular than the roving from which it is made.)

On completion of the draw the yarn is of the right count but it has not yet got sufficient twist to make it strong enough. Rotation of the spindles is, therefore, continued until enough twist has been introduced.

The next operation is backing-off. The spindles are turned backwards in order to release the few turns of yarn which are on the bare portion of the spindle blade, and at the same time the faller wire is pressed down into contact with the yarn. During winding the clove is moved steadily towards the spindles and the yarn is wound onto the upper conical surface of the cop by rotating the spindles in the spinning direction while at the same time guiding the yarn by means of the moveable faller. At the end of the winding operation when the clove, still locked, has been returned to its original position close to the spindle tips, the faller is lifted clear

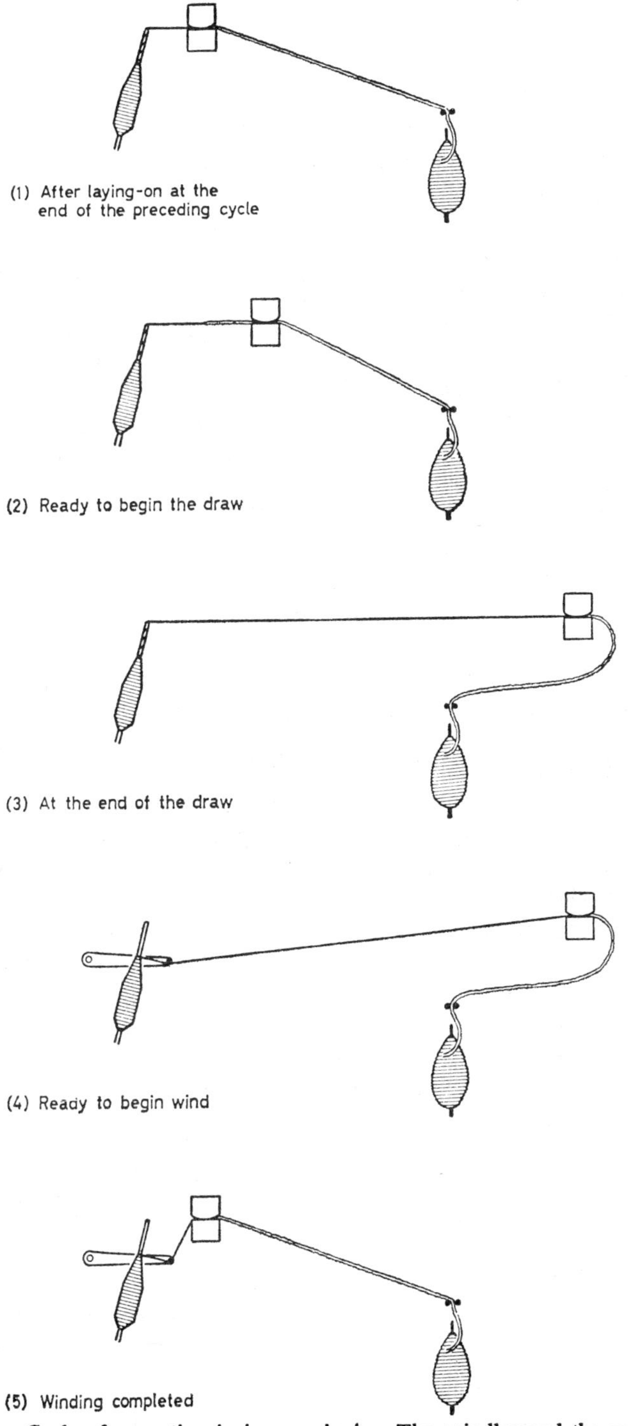

Fig 5. Cycle of operation in jenny spinning. The spindles and the roving creel are fixed; only the clove moves

of the yarn and the spindles make a few turns to lay-on yarn coils from the top of the cop to the spindle tip.

Once the principle of jenny spinning had been established, development consisted of changes in the construction and arrangement of the elements to permit more and more spindles to be operated by one person. We do know that the sixteen-spindle machine of the 1770 patent was driven by the right hand, the fly being mounted with its axis substantially vertical and to the right of the machine. The clove was controlled entirely by the left hand. During winding the left foot, by means of a treadle, moved the faller wire to guide the yarn evenly onto the surface of the cop chase.

This was not a particularly convenient arrangement and it was not long before the more familiar machine was evolved in which the fly, mounted with its axis horizontal and above the yarn sheet, drove the spindles via a lay shaft in the form of a tin roller. At about the same time an ingenious device was introduced to enable the operator, when winding, to control both the clove and the faller by means of his left hand only. These improvements enabled very much larger jennies to be made. With the early design the length of the draw was limited to about 1 yd, but within a few years draws of about 54 in were usual and the number of spindles had been increased to 60, 80 and occasionally even 120 spindles.

2

Samuel Crompton

THE cotton trade was a vigorous and rapidly growing young industry when Crompton came on the scene. Cotton textiles had been introduced into Britain by the East India Company in the seventeenth century. They became so popular for fashionable ladies' wear, as well as for household uses, that the established woollen and linen industries complained loudly that they were being ruined. To protect the home industries the use of cotton goods 'as apparel or furniture' was, in 1700, prohibited under heavy penalty. Later, complete prohibition gave way to restrictions and a heavy duty. As technology of cotton manufacture in this country advanced, public interest eventually prevailed and an Act of 1774 for the first time permitted the 'use and wear of any new manufactured stuffs wholly made of Cotton', subject only to a duty of 3d per square yd on being printed.

In this same year Samuel Crompton, then twenty-one years old, first began to build the spinning machine which was later to be known as the mule. Samuel lived with his widowed mother, Betty, and his crippled uncle, Alexander Crompton, in the old manor house of Hall i' th' Wood, a mile or so out of Bolton in Lancashire. (It is now open to the public as a Crompton Museum.) He had worked from early childhood, first at the spinning wheel and later at the loom. Two years after Hargreaves invented the jenny, Samuel, a boy of sixteen, was hard at work operating one of the new machines with eight spindles. For five years, under his mother's supervision, he continued with this occupation and studied at evening school. The shortcomings of the simple jenny vexed him and he determined to make a better device.

There were a number of empty rooms in the old manor in which Crompton could enjoy privacy and carry out his experiments. Cameron records that many years later, Crompton in describing the development of his machine, wrote:

> . . . some one or other of these rooms I constantly kept for my private use, no one knowing what I was about; and here the whole of my powers both of body and mind were concentrated in one continued endeavour to accomplish the object of my pursuit.

Crompton was not an untutored man who stumbled upon his invention by accident. The son of a skilled craftsman, he was himself a man of some culture and education, a good mathematician and a musician with a wide knowledge of classical music. Most important of all, his grasp of the technology was such that he had the confidence to devote all his talents to the solution of the engineering problems involved in the construction of the new machine. It is virtually certain that others before Crompton had considered the possibility of combining the drafting rollers of Arkwright's water frame and the spinning action of Hargreaves' jenny: but the achievement of this combination posed many problems. Perhaps the most difficult of these was the need, during spinning, for accurately-controlled translatory motion of the rapidly rotating spindles, relative to the precisely driven drafting rollers.

Crompton solved the problem in the manner shown in Fig 6. The spindles, driving bands and drum of a typical jenny were mounted on a wheeled carriage running on rails fixed to the floor. An ingenious arrangement of guide pulleys permitted the spindles to be coupled at all times to a fixed fly while the carriage was moved along the rails under the control of draw bands. Both the drafting rollers and the draw bands were also coupled to the fly during the draw but were disengaged from the fly during supplementary twisting, backing-off and winding. The sequence of operations for a complete cycle was:

1. With roller and carriage drives engaged the fly was turned

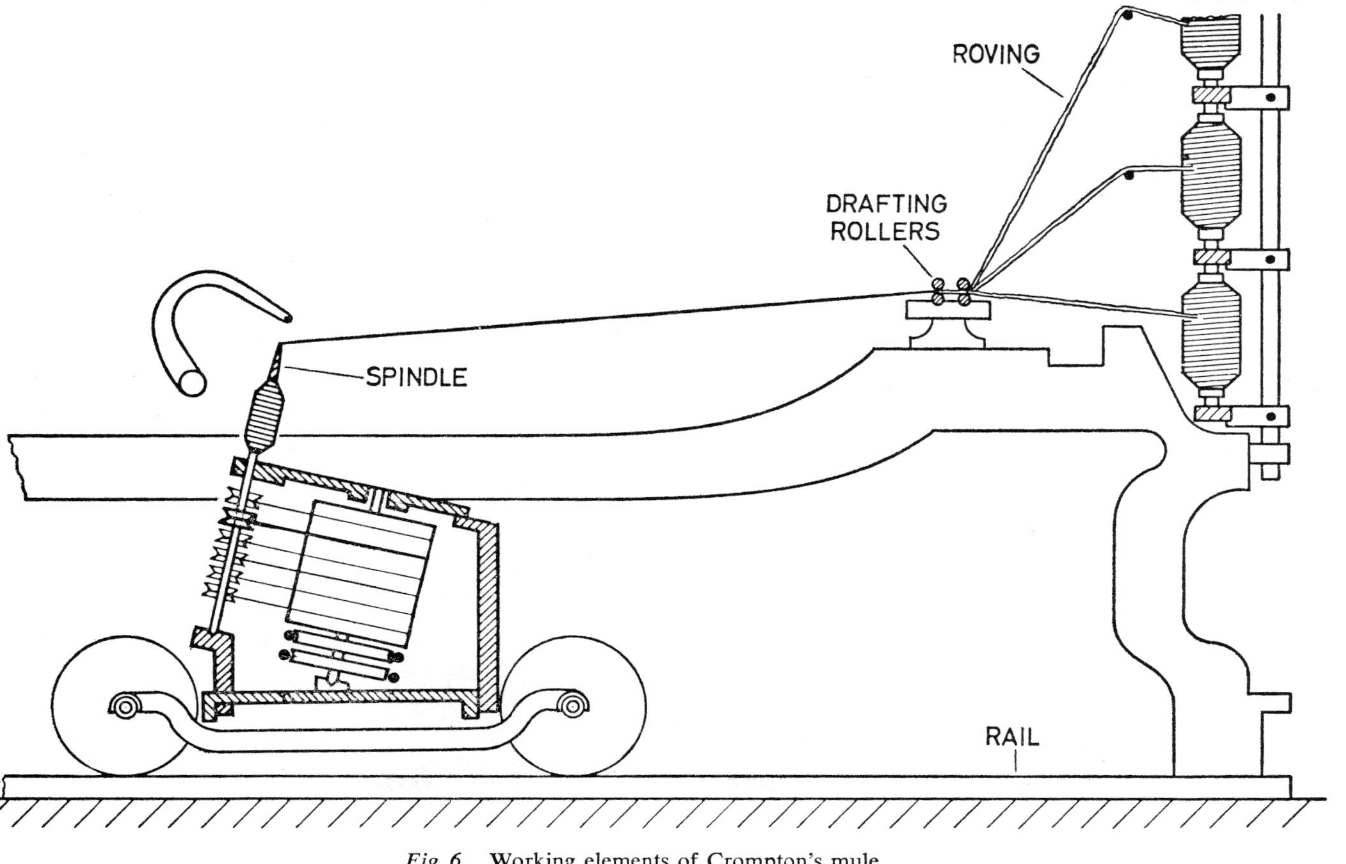

Fig 6. Working elements of Crompton's mule

briskly by means of a large cranked handle. This simultaneously caused (*a*) the rollers to turn and deliver drafted slubbing; (*b*) the spindles to turn and so twist the slubbing into a soft yarn; (*c*) the carriage carrying the spindles to move from the rollers more rapidly than the slubbing was being delivered and thus level the yarn by drawing out the thicker places.

2. On completion of the draw the roller and carriage drives were disengaged but rotation of the fly was continued until the required total amount of twist had been inserted in the yarn.

3. The fly was used to turn the spindles backwards and so unwind the coils of yarn between the top of the cop and the tip of the spindle blade.

4. The fly was turned in the spinning direction to wind up the yarn. The right hand was used to turn the fly while the left hand was used to guide the yarn into the form of a cop by means of a rocking shaft and a yarn guide-wire mounted on the carriage and known as the faller. This action tended to draw the carriage in towards the rollers, and the tension thus developed in the yarn was controlled either by assisting the movement of the carriage by pressure of the operator's knee to reduce tension, or by restraining the carriage with the hand controlling the faller to increase tension.

5. On completion of winding the faller was returned to a position clear of the yarn, with the fly continuing to rotate so as to lay the yarn in an open spiral from the top of the cop to the spindle tip. During this operation the roller and carriage drives were re-engaged in readiness for the next draw.

Construction of the first machine was a slow business. Crompton worked alone with only simple tools, and it is said that in order to raise money for the purchase of tools and materials he used to play the fiddle at the Bolton Theatre for a fee of 1s 6d (7½ p) per performance. However, he persevered with the work for five long, arduous years until, in his own words, 'I . . . at length succeeded to my utmost desire, at the expence of every shilling I had in the world.'

Completion of the work coincided with the machine-breaking riots of 1779, and Crompton felt obliged to dismantle his machine and hide the parts in various closets and attics in the rambling old

Page 35: (above) Firwood Fold, Crompton's birthplace; (below) Hall i' th' Wood. Crompton built his mule in the attic of the Hall, which is now open to the public as a textile museum

Page 36: (above) Mule owned by Crompton. The carriage has been drastically shortened. Originally it probably had about 120 spindles; (below) Spinning on late period jennies. The spinner has almost finished putting up the mule on the left, whilst that to the right is nearing the end of its draw; c 1825

hall. Later in the year, when things had quietened down again, the parts were taken out of hiding, re-assembled and set to work.

The original machine has not survived and little is known of the details of its construction except that it had forty-eight spindles and was largely made from wood. Wooden machinery was, of course, very common at this date and Crompon preferred to work with wood. A few metal parts were used and for these Crompton had the help of a neighbouring blacksmith and the occasional use of his smithy. By Arkwright's standards the drafting rollers were very crude indeed. Where Arkwright used fluted metal rollers, driven by toothed gearing, beautifully finished by Kay, the clock-maker, Crompton had only wooden rollers driven by pulleys and bands. To improve the grip of these wooden rollers he set dents of brass reed wire into the surface, a resourceful expedient but a poor substitute for an accurately machined metal roller.

Despite the limitations of its construction the new machine was immediately successful. It spun yarns of a quality never before seen. Although his original intention had been to spin yarn only for his own weaving, Crompton soon began to do a little spinning for other weavers. At first he was delighted to obtain a price of 14s (70 p) per lb for spinning 40's yarn, and a short time later, as his skill increased, he was able to spin 60's and get 25s (£1·25) per lb. It was at that time thought impossible to spin a cotton yarn of 80's count in Britain but before long this too was accomplished, and the quality was so high that the staggering price of 42s (£2·10) per lb was commanded.

This was much more rewarding than weaving. At this time a skilled and diligent weaver was able to earn between 30s and 40s (£1·50–£2) for a week's work. We do not know exactly how productive the first mule was, but by assuming that it had a draw of 54 in and could be operated at the rate of one draw per minute a reasonable estimate is possible. This works out at about 1 lb of 60's yarn for twelve hours' work so that in a sixty-hour week (by no means excessive at that time), Crompton was able to earn four or five times as much by spinning as he could by weaving. The temptation was very great and he soon gave up weaving altogether and devoted all his efforts to spinning.

His new-found affluence was celebrated by the purchase of a large silver watch, made especially for him at a cost of five guineas. He also married and set up home in a cottage attached to the Hall. The prodigious output of superlative yarn did not, of course, pass unnoticed. Merchants and their agents besieged the Hall, anxious to buy yarn of such excellent quality but even more anxious to find out how it was made.

The Cromptons tried hard to keep their secret, but month by month the pressures mounted until Samuel reluctantly came to the conclusion that it was impossible to keep the importunate enquirers at bay any longer. He had no patent or the means to purchase one but saw a solution in the suggestion of John Pilkington, a well-to-do cotton merchant in Bolton and a personal friend. Pilkington's solution to the problem was that a subscription list be opened with the agreement that in return for the subscription Crompton would make his invention free to all.

Both Crompton and Pilkington, appreciating the value of the machine to the industry, were confident that the response would be generous. In this they were sadly mistaken. A facsimile of the agreement by which Crompton surrendered his invention is reproduced in French's *Life*. Eighty-two firms or individuals in the industry signed this agreement which ran:

> Bolton, November 20th 1780
>
> We whose names are hereunto subscribed have agreed to give, and do hereby promise to pay unto Samuel Crompton at the Hall in the wood near Bolton the several sums opposite to our names as a reward for his improvement in Spinning. Several of the principal Tradesmen in Manchester, Bolton &c., having seen his Machine, approve of it, and are of opinion that it would be of the greatest utility to make it generally known to which end a contribution is desired from every well wisher of trade.

The 'several sums' ranged from 5s 6d (27½ p) to one guinea (£1·5) and totalled £70.9.6 (£70·47½). Even this niggardly sum was not paid in full and in the event Crompton received only about £60. He later complained 'I received as much by way of subscriptions as built me a new machine with only four spindles more than the one I had given up—the old one having forty-eight, the new one fifty-two spindles.'

Although some of the subscribers denounced the inventor as an imposter and withheld their promised contribution the 'Hall i' th' Wood Wheel' was immediately successful. At this time all fine yarns suitable for the weaving of muslins were imported from India and fine cotton cloths were a luxury available only to the well-to-do. The availability of home-spun fine yarns greatly stimulated the demand and the new machine became known as the 'Muslin Wheel'. Great numbers were built almost immediately and during the next ten years the British cotton trade increased fivefold and Baines recorded that:

> The increase of weavers kept pace with the increase of spinners; and all classes of workmen in this trade received extravagant wages; such as were necessary to draw from other trades the amount of labour for which the cotton trade offered profitable employment.

This most spectacular boom arose as a result of a number of factors. It would be wrong to ascribe it wholly to Crompton's invention. The inventor himself, however, took a jaundiced view of the turn of events. It had been his intention to build himself a machine which would earn him an easy competence. Instead he had provided a bonanza for the swaggering upstart speculators who were anathema to his frugal, retiring nature. As he saw more and more men-of-the-world use his invention to gain a flamboyant prosperity that was far removed from his own way of life he became a man with a grievance. Although he was by nature quite unable to enjoy the thrust and strife of the commercial jungle he envied these men. That he had succeeded completely as an inventor was not enough. Above everything else he would have succeeded as a businessman but he could not: the humiliation of this failure was torment to his soul and haunted him to the grave.

For a time Crompton combined farming and spinning at Oldhams, a farm in the township of Sharples, near Bolton. This was not completely satisfactory and in 1791 he gave up spinning altogether and returned to Bolton to work as a muslin weaver. This was a time of unprecedented prosperity for weavers. They wore top-boots and ruffed shirts and would parade the streets of the town with a £5 note stuck carelessly in their hat bands. Under these buoyant trading conditions Crompton fared quite comfortably, but when prices for weaving began to fall he soon found himself in difficult circumstances. From this situation he was rescued by two Manchester spinners, John Kennedy and George Lee, who in 1800 promoted a subscription on his behalf. About £500 was raised, clearing his immediate debts and enabling him to set up a business based on the running of two large mules and the employment of fifty or so weavers working to his order in their own homes.

This venture was not altogether unsuccessful, but in 1811 Crompton decided to petition Parliament for what he felt to be his due. To gain evidence in suport of his petition he toured the textile districts of England and Scotland. He was himself astonished by what he found; to the total spinning capacity of the realm Hargreaves' jenny and Arkwright's water frame together contributed less than 500,000 spindles, whereas his own mule provided more than 4,500,000.

At this time such petitions were not uncommon. Cartwright, the inventor of the power loom, had received a grant of £10,000 in response to a similar petition and Crompton had sanguine expectations that he himself would receive a substantially greater sum. Early in March 1812 Parliament set up a committee to consider the petition. A great deal of evidence was called and eventually, to the bitter disappointment of the petitioner, a grant of only £5,000 was made in late June. Crompton, now in his fifty-ninth year, returned to Bolton and his muslin weaving. What remained of the grant after payment of his considerable expenses was invested in a bleach croft at Darwen. Managed by his son, George, this business failed to prosper and was sold by auction seven years later. A little later the cotton-manufacturing business in Bolton, in which Crompton was partnered by his son William, ran into difficulties and was broken up.

This was the end of Crompton's working life. A last subscription was launched on his behalf by his fellow townsmen and sufficient money was raised to buy him an annuity of £63. For his remaining years (he died in 1827 at the age of seventy-four) Crompton was almost entirely dependent on this pittance for his simple needs.

3

The Mule Jenny

IT is commonly the lot of the inventor to spend frustrating years convincing the world of the merits of his inventions. As Sir William Petty remarked in his *A treatise on Taxes and Contributions* (1679):

> Altho' the inventor, oftentimes drunk with the opinion of his own merit, thinks all the world will invade and encroach upon him, yet I have observed that the generality of men will scarce be hired to make use of the new practices, which themselves have not thoroughly tried, and which length of time hath not vindicated from latent inconvenience; so as when a new invention is first propounded, in the beginning every man objects, and the poor inventor runs the gantloop of all petulant wits; every man finding his several flaw, no man approving it unless mended according to his own device. Now not one of an hundred outlives this torture, and those that do are so changed by the various contrivances of others, that not any one man can pretend to the invention of the whole, nor will agree about their respective shares in the parts. And moreover this is commonly so long a-doing, that the poor inventor is either dead, or disabled by the debts contracted to pursue his design; and withal railed upon as a projector, or worse, by those who joyned their money in partnership with his wit; so as the said inventor and his pretences are wholly lost and vanished.

Yet this was not Crompton's fate; all the world did indeed invade and encroach upon him. His invention was taken up and used on a scale beyond his wildest dreams. Nor was he denied recognition as a man of genius. From the start he was universally acknowledged as the sole inventor of the most nearly perfect of all spinning machines.

Crompton was in no way concerned with the further development of his invention. From the moment of its disclosure to subscribers in 1780 there was no lack of hands and minds eager to set the new machine to work: but Crompton found to his sorrow that he was unable to contend with men of the world. There is no record of his contributing in any way to subsequent developments.

Almost immediately Henry Stones, an ingenious mechanic of Horwich, constructed a new mule in a most workmanlike manner. The rollers were of metal, and toothed gearing was used to replace Crompton's bands and pulleys. With this construction about 100 spindles could be driven by one man. Baker of Bury and Hargreaves of Taddington also manufactured mules to meet the considerable demand. The latter is credited with the first use of a scroll instead of a plain drum to control the draw bands. Thus he achieved smoother acceleration and deceleration of the carriage.

Although these first hand-driven mules had a prodigious output by the standards of the day, it was not long before atttempts were made to apply animal or water power to even larger mules. Because of the discontinuous nature of the mule spinning cycle it was not simply a matter of coupling the machine to a horse gin or to a water wheel. Completely powered operation was to challenge inventive genius for the next half century. It was soon found possible, however, to harness any available rotary power source to the exhausting business of driving spindles at high speed during the draw and during twisting at the head.

William Kelly of New Lanark is sometimes credited with being the first to apply power to the mule, and there is no doubt that he had done so by 1790. This is made clear in correspondence between Kelly and John Kennedy concerning Kelly's application in 1792 for a patent for a completely automatic mule. Kennedy too was deeply involved in the business of building ever bigger and better mules.

The firm of McConnell & Kennedy arose out of a machine-making business set up in Ancoats by James McConnell around 1788. Originally the chief concern of the firm was the building of mules but in 1789, when two mules of 144 and 120 spindles were left on their hands after a customer stopped payment, interest was broadened to include spinning. The copy letter-books for the early years of the firm's existence (it later became an important member of the Fine Spinners & Doublers Association, now part of Courtaulds' Northern Textile Division) are still extant and tell something of the development of the mule during this interesting period.

In correspondence with Messrs Taylor & Heywood of Duffield near Derby, during February 1795, Messrs McConnell & Kennedy say:

> We shall be very glad to make you 5 mules of 144 spindles but would recommend larger if the room permits. 180 spindles is as few as any we have made for this some time, which we sell at £38 and 144 spindles at £33 to spin by hand—the gearing for water spinning would be charged according to the manner it was done.
>
> It is difficult to fix what number of spindles may be most profitable as what was thought best only two years ago is now thought too small. 216 is made to run as light now as 144 used to do then; though it cannot be said to do as much work in proportion to the number of spindles. We are making now from 180 to 288 spindles and as far as we can judge of the future from the past would not recommend a building less than ten yards wide within which would hold about 240 with plenty of room at the end.

There can be no doubt that mules with more than 200 spindles were already being made and that power was being used to drive them. The correspondence also contains details of the dimensions of the completed machines from which it appears that the standard spindle gauge (ie the distance between centres of adjacent spindles) was 1¼ in and that the length occupied by the headstock and framing was 2 ft 6 in.

On 15 April McConnell & Kennedy are apologetic about the supply position. Exceptional pressure of work is pleaded as the reason why the new mules cannot be completed in less than four weeks. The mules were duly made and dispatched some forty miles through the High Peak of Derbyshire by cart on 'Tewsday 26th May' and arrangements made for a young man to go to Cromford and supervise erection. The new machines must have been commissioned most expeditiously, for in a letter of 6 July McConnell & Kennedy are commenting on the quality of the yarn produced and replying to Taylor & Heywood's request for a quotation for more mules to the same pattern. The reply strikes a still topical note, '. . . owing to the advance on Timber, Iron and Wages . . .' a price increase of approximately 10 per cent has been made.

At this time McConnell & Kennedy acted also as yarn agents and made arrangements to take yarn from spinners who had bought or were about to buy their mules. The terms and requirements are set out very simply in a letter of 28 July 1795:

> We would take 40 or 50 lbs a week of 90's & 95's in the cop if good and full counts. The price would be near 1d per hank when laid down here if very good. What we have in one month would pay you for the next. When packed well in a Tea Box it will carry without being much hurt.
>
> p.s. What Wraps 88–89–90–91 and 92 we call 90, from 93 to 97–95.

The fall in the price of yarn since Crompton first spun 80's and received 42s (£2·10) per lb for it is striking. The price for 95's is now barely 8s (40 p) per lb and that only 'if very good'.

Up to about this time mules had been considered singly and were made, as was Crompton's original machine, with the headstock to the extreme right of the carriage. This allowed the spinner to operate the fly with his right hand and control the carriage and faller with his left hand. Before the application of power the spinner was fully occupied throughout the cycle of operations and, naturally, could tend only one mule. With power it was a simple matter to arrange that the draw could proceed without supervision, the drive to the carriage being automatically disengaged on completion of the draw. It was also arranged that twisting at the head would continue until the required number of turns of twist had been put into the yarn before the belt driving the fly was moved automatically onto the loose pulley. In connection with his patent of 1792, which is concerned with completely automatic operation, Kelly refers to the already well-established 'apparatus or machinery (which) allowed the mule to stop in the common way on receiving the full complement of twist'.

When equipped with this 'apparatus or machinery' the spinner had only to back–off and put-up the mule (ie wind on the yarn and return the carriage in readiness for the next draw). It was quickly appreciated that as these operations took rather less than half of the total cycle time, it was possible for one spinner to operate two mules. Who did this first is not recorded, but certainly Kelly did so in 1790 'by placing the mules right and left'.

Exactly how Kelly's mules were arranged is not clear: but Wright of Manchester is credited with making the first mule with spindles to both left and right of the headstock. There is no doubt, however, as to the arrangement of the mules supplied by McConnell & Kennedy to Ainsworths of Preston in 1797. Correspondence of September of that year gives considerable detail of what the machinery maker had to offer. The basic mule with three lines of rollers (Crompton's had only two) cost 4s 6d per spindle. Gearing for water or steam power was 3d per spindle extra and an epicyclic two-speed gear was available for a further 3d per spindle. Ainsworths placed an order and in McConnell & Kennedy's letter of acceptance of 19 September the arrangement is described clearly with the aid of a sketch:

> . . . to contain 372 each at $1\frac{3}{8}$ Inh. distance with the Rim (ie the fly) in the middle and the whole frame to measure 46 feet 4 inches outside with one end to hold three heads of rollers more than the other which will make it about four feet longer than the other as below

46 FEET 4 INCHES LONG

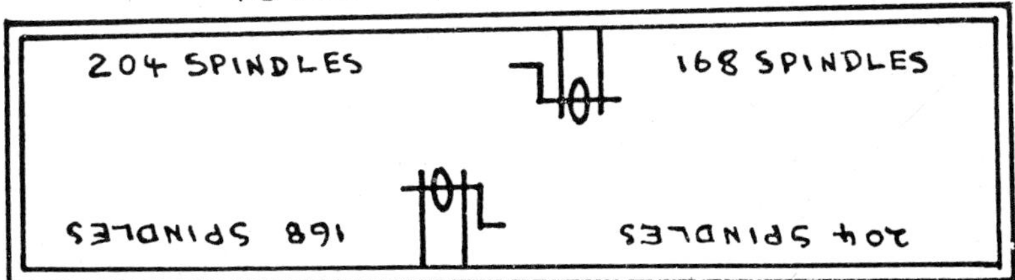

The sketch was intended to indicate to the customer that the two mules would be built face to face, as are the mules shown in the plates on pages 36, 133 and 151. Standing by the fly, facing either mule, the spinner would have 204 spindles to his left and 168 to his right. On turning to face the other mule he would see exactly the same arrangement, the part of the mule to the left of the fly being about four ft longer than the part to the right of the fly in each case. The sketch crudely depicts the headstock frame, the fly and the cranked handle by which the fly was turned. The two halves of each mule are not drawn but are indicated by the words '204 spindles' and '168 spindles', the inversion of the words in the lower mule being intended to convey the information that the mules are face to face.

This arrangement became extremely popular. The spinner had to do no more than turn on his heel as he switched his attention from one mule to the other; yet the mules were in no sense 'handed'—they were absolutely identical. The arrangement became, in fact, so firmly established that even when the introduction of the self-actor made manual control no longer necessary, mules continued to be made in the same offset fashion and arranged in the same way. The mules shown on page 36 are of a later date but show the arrangement. The spinner has almost finished putting-up the mule on the left while that to the right is nearing the end of its draw.

The pace of life in those days must have been distinctly hectic for the captains of industry. New mills were being erected wherever water could be harnessed, and not all machinery was built by professionals. Most machinery makers were prepared to supply the machined metal components and let the customer himself build the frames from timber, although McConnell & Kennedy, in quoting for the supply of a 'do-it-yourself kit' for a 240-spindle mule, gave the warning: 'But making Machinery is generally very expensive to those who are not in the habit of it.'

Some idea of the pace set by the leading firms can be gleaned from McConnell & Kennedy's copy letter-book for 1797:

To Messrs Boulton and Watt
Birmingham
12th May 1797.

We are beginning to build a Cotton Factory, for which we shall want a Steam Engine of about Twelve or Fourteen horses power

> by the beginning of September. Therefore this is to request that you will favour us as soon as possible with the particular dimensions of the Engine and Boiler Houses and likewise the different prices for Engines of these powers. Subjoined is a rough draft of the intended plan, which you will please to look over and point out where it may be wrong. We are to be supplied with water from a Canal by pipes through a Street of 10 yards wide, and which is to be returned again to the Canal. The Canal is about six feet deep the bottom may be three feet below the cellar floor of the factory and we suppose the top of the Condensing cistern to stand 3 feet 4 inches above the cellar floor; now if the centre of the Rotative Shaft could be 4f. 6i. higher than the top of the Condensing cistern it would go straight to the drum shaft which would require the connecting rod to be so much shorter. The Engine and Boiler Houses we wish to be kept as low as may be as it is intended to build over them at another time, and if it would answer to have the chimney as in the plan it would we think be more convenient on some other accounts. As Mule Spinning requires a considerable heat in the rooms; pray could any advantage be got from the Engine pipe by using it as a Stove for that purpose. Having mentioned what appears to us most convenient we wish you only to observe as far as may be proper and shall be glad if you will send a plan of the foundation as soon as possible as it must be laid in a few days.

In 1797 it was a long journey from Manchester to Birmingham. The construction of rotary steam engines was in its infancy and the letter raised quite a number of technical points. Despite this, Boulton & Watt made a prompt reply. McConnell & Kennedy were equally prompt and only ten days after the first inquiry a firm order was placed for '. . . a Steam engine of Sixteen horses power; which we wish you to have ready for the beginning of Septr. next...'

The mill was built and the engine duly installed. Sixteen horse power (hp) now seems an incredibly small amount of power to drive a whole mill, but it must be remembered that only eight years earlier James McConnell's first mill was driven by two Irishmen. During the eight-year interval between the Irishmen and the 16 hp engine, a gin turned by two horses had been used. The 16 hp engine drove all the machinery in a mill of approximately 8,400 spindles. If we assume that three-quarters of the power was used to drive the mules, we get a rating of 700 spindles per hp. This fits reasonably with the fact that a mule of 120 spindles was about the limit for purely manual operation a few years earlier: but it is a surprisingly high figure compared with the sixty to eighty spindles per hp usual in mule mills built towards the end of the nineteenth century. The explanation is, of course, that the early powered mules were run very slowly indeed because of the high cost of power from the engines of the day. A typical Boulton & Watt engine had a specific fuel consumption of about 15 lb of coal per hp hour but, by 1900, triple expansion engines of about 1,000 hp were using less than $1\frac{1}{2}$ lb of coal per hp hour.

By 1800, just twenty years after the principle of the mule became public property, enormous advances had been made. The mule had become by far the most popular spinning machine and the price of 80's cotton yarn had been reduced from 42s to 6s 10d (34 p) per lb. The new availability of fine cottons only served to stimulate their demand and more and more would-be Arkwrights were entering the industry determined to make a fortune out of the new spinning machines. As cotton manufacture, and particularly spinning, became highly competitive so did the pressures to reduce production costs. Despite the developments which had taken place, the final stage of spinning remained by far the most expensive single operation and it was here that efforts at cost reduction were concentrated.

The attack was made on two fronts. The more imaginative approach was to make the mule completely self-acting so that unskilled or juvenile labour could be employed, and for many years inventors struggled towards this goal with only limited success. The less imaginative but more directly rewarding approach was to refine the design of manually controlled mules and thereby enable one spinner to operate more and more spindles.

The limitation of the early manually powered mules was the sheer muscle power required to drive spindles at high speeds. The application of water or steam power removed this limitation and the number of spindles per mule rose very quickly from about 100 to upwards of 250. At the same time the spinning speed was increased and a two-speed gear to give very rapid twisting at the head was introduced. It was then found that with 300 or more spindles the task of putting-up the mule became rather laborious. Although much larger mules were built, it was generally felt that the extra physical burden made the very large mules scarcely worthwhile. The obvious next step was to provide a little mechanical help for the spinner during putting-up.

It is difficult to say just when the first putting-up motion was made. Evan Leigh, in his book *Science of Modern Cotton Spinning*, claims that he made the first successful one in 1832. There is no doubt, however, that DeJongh's unsuccessful self-actor of 1825 included a basically similar device and it seems very likely that putting-up motions of one sort or another were made within months of the first realisation that the spinner needed help at this part of the cycle.

Briefly, putting-up motions were devices by which power was applied through a slack belt or a slipping clutch to help rotation of the fly during the inward run of the carriage or, in some cases, to help directly the motion of the carriage. Adjustment was provided so that the spinner could regulate the action to suit the count being spun and the frictional conditions present in the machine at a particular time. The first putting-up motion was probably no more than an arrangement whereby the main driving belt did not go fully onto the loose pulley on completion of the draw. Instead it maintained sufficient contact with the fast pulley to be of material help in rotating the fly during putting-up without having so strong a grip as to take command of the situation.

Aided by a putting-up motion spinners were able to operate even more spindles. Evan Leigh records:

> Instead of 300 spindles mules were now built of from 600 to 1200 spindles, and the price of spinning was reduced about one half. Singular as it may seem the operatives also shared in the benefit, for they could earn more money on the new machinery with less physical toil; and those who were temporarily thrown out of work by the changes were soon absorbed by the rapid extension of the cotton manufacture which took place about this time (c 1830), partly from the cheapening of production and partly from other causes.

After the introduction of the putting-up motion no major changes were made in the design of manually controlled mules. From about

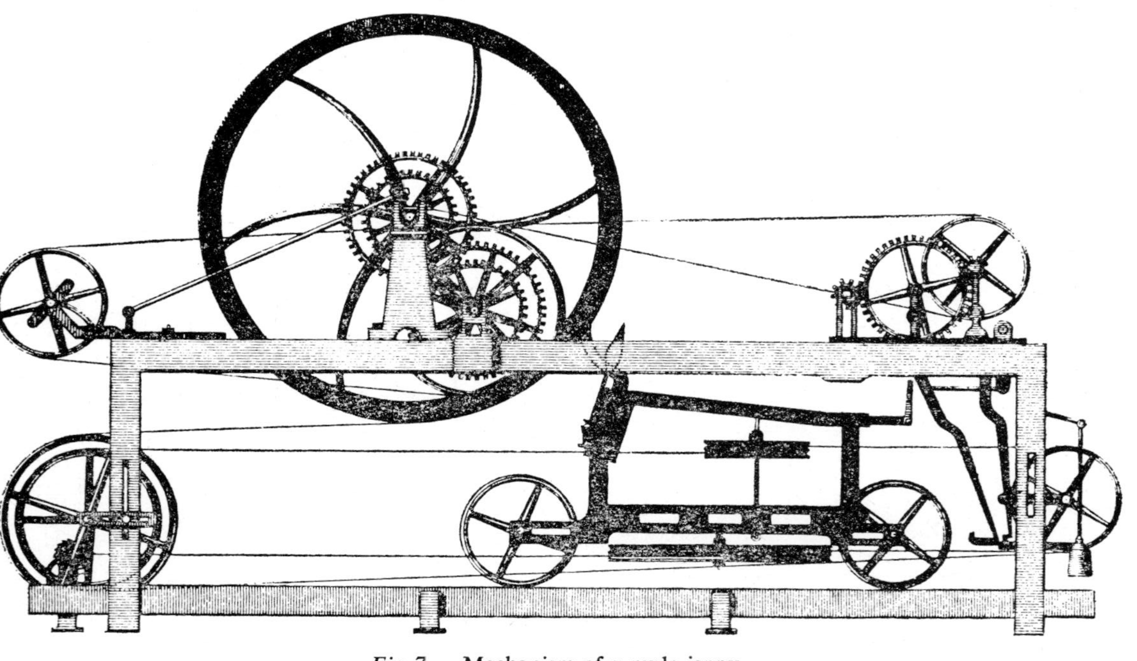

Fig 7. Mechanism of a mule jenny

1830 onwards the self-acting mule began to be used increasingly for the coarser yarns. The manually controlled mule, which soon came to be known as the mule jenny or hand mule to distinguish it from the self-actor, continued to be preferred for the finer yarns. In about 1860 Evan Leigh wrote, 'Hand mule spinning is now generally employed from No 60's upwards,' and twenty years later, in the *Proceedings of the Institution of Mechanical Engineers*, Eli Spencer wrote: 'For spinning yarns of medium fine counts, say up to No 90, the self-acting mule has now almost entirely superseded the hand mule.' As Mr Spencer was the technical director of Messrs Platt Bros, a company very proud of its contribution to the development of self-acting mules, we can suppose that his statement was something of a boast and that, in fact, many hand mules continued to be used even for medium-fine counts fifty years after the introduction of the self-actor.

By the end of the nineteenth century highly complex self-actors were able to spin even the finest counts, although some diehards maintained that for best fine yarns the hand mule could not be beaten. Certainly hand mules remained in limited commercial use well into the present century and some are still used in the Welsh craft industry. As recently as 1964 the author visited the spinning and weaving mill of J. T. Vaughan at Aber Cegir near Machynlleth, where two mules were then in use. One was a self-actor built by Whitely Bros of Huddersfield about 1870 and the other was a hand mule of about 220 spindles built by the local Dolgoch Co in 1855. Mr Vaughan, who has since died, was extremely conservative in his views on automation generally and on its application to spinning in particular. Although proud of the fact that Roberts, the inventor of the self-actor, was a man of his own county (Montgomery), he contended that really good cops for the shuttle could not be wound on a self-actor. His own practice was to make only his twist yarns on the self-actor, preferring, as he was also the weaver, to spin his weft on the hand mule. As hand-mule spinning is inordinately laborious in a mill where a self-actor is available, there can be no doubt that Mr Vaughan was sincere in his contention.

4

Birth of the Self-actor

THE invention of the mule made mechanised spinning of fine yarns a practical proposition for the first time in Britain. The initial demand for the new yarns far exceeded the supply, and prices were fixed only in relation to the cost of importing hand-spun yarns from the East. For a time the possession of any sort of mule was virtually 'a licence to print bank notes'. Naturally this state of affairs could not continue and before long the market became keenly competitive. It was, however, a rapidly expanding market and the incentive to increase spinning productivity was very great indeed.

Crompton, with his first machine, could earn a princely salary operating only forty-eight spindles and producing about 1 lb of 60's yarn per day. This demanded an average spindle speed, during the working day, of about 1,700 revolutions per minute (rpm) and probably required an average power input of about $\frac{1}{16}$ hp. Six years later, in 1785, the number of spindles had been more than doubled, but because of the physical effort required to drive them, the average speed of the spindles had remained roughly the same or perhaps fallen a little. Even so the operator was himself required to provide about $\frac{1}{10}$ hp, an output which can only be achieved by a fit man prepared to work very strenuously.

Naturally it was not long before animal, water or steam power was harnessed to the mule and by 1895 mules of 240 spindles were operating with average spindle speeds of about 2,250 rpm. At this time each mule required about $\frac{1}{3}$ hp to drive it (750 spindles per hp). As power became cheaper speeds increased, and by 1825 spindles were being run at about 3,000 rpm. It may seem a modest increase over a period of thirty years but it must be appreciated that at this speed, largely because of aerodynamic factors, the power required to rotate a spindle and cop is roughly proportional to the cube of the speed. This means that the power required to drive a given number of spindles is increased almost 2½ times on increasing the speed from 2,250 to 3,000 rpm. Thus the typical 600 spindle mule of 1825 required about 2 hp to drive it.

The combined effect of increasing the spindle speed and increasing the number of spindles per mule, and later the practice of operating the mules as pairs, greatly reduced the labour required for spinning. Today it is usual to express the productivity of textile operatives in terms of OHP, that is, in terms of the number of operative hours needed to process 100 lb of material. If a machine carrying out a particular process is tended by three operatives and has an output of 25 lb of processed material an hour, that process is said to have an OHP requirement of 12.

Using the most efficient modern machinery the spinning of 80's cotton yarn requires about 40 OHP today. Before the invention of the mule, 80's yarn was not spun in Britain and we have no reliable data as to the rate at which Indian hand-spinners spun that count. It is probable, however, that the OHP figure was in excess of 50,000. Crompton's first machine reduced this immediately to about 2,000. The next generation of mules, with around 100 spindles, brought a further reduction to about 1,000.

With the introduction of powered mules worked in pairs, some ancillary labour, usually female or juvenile, became necessary in addition to the spinner: but the OHP figure continued to fall. In 1795 a man and a boy were able to operate a pair of powered mules, each of 240 spindles driven at 2,250 rpm. With this arrangement the OHP for 80's was brought down to 300. From this time onwards progress became very much slower as the limit of manually controlled mules was approached. Even so a considerable improvement was effected during the next thirty years. The 600-spindle mules of 1825 were run at 3,000 rpm and each pair required only one man and two boys to run them—an OHP for 80's of only 135.

The reduction in labour required naturally reduced the cost of spinning. In addition, from 1810 onwards the price of cotton began to fall as the growing demand induced more intensive cultivation of the crop in various parts of the world. Thus the price of yarn fell steadily throughout the fifty years following the invention of the mule. The changing pattern can be seen in Table 1.

TABLE 1

Year	*Price of 1 lb of fine cotton*	*Price of 1 lb of 80's*	*Cost of spinning 1 lb of 80's*	*lbs of cotton used in Britain (in millions)*
1780	2/3	42/-	39/9	5·2
1785	2/-	28/6	26/6	18·4
1790	1/9	21/6	19/9	31·4
1795	2/3	11/4	9/1	26·4
1800	2/9	9/9	7/-	56·0
1810	2/2	4/3	2/1	132·0
1830	-/11	2/7	1/8	263·9

The development of the mule had proceeded far beyond the dreams of the inventor. The application of steam-power to mules housed in enormous factories was far from Crompton's design 'and no man lamented more the changes thus brought about in the lives of the people'. It was, however, very much the design of a number of extremely able and determined people. The success of the manually controlled mule was not enough; it merely served to encourage those inventors who from 1790 onwards were bent on the achievement of a completely automatic machine.

The difficulties were formidable. There were many failures and a number of near-successes. One of the earliest near-misses was made by William Kelly of Lanark Mills. In an account of his experience, written for Edward Baines in 1829, Kelly gives a very clear picture of what he achieved:

> I first applied water-power to common mules in the year 1790, that is, we drove the mules by water, but put them up, (that is the carriage or spindle frame) in the common way, by applying the hand to the flywheel.
>
> From the above date I constantly had in view the self-acting mule, and trying to bring it into use; and having got it to do very

well for coarse numbers, I took out the patent in the summer 1792. The object then was to spin with young people, like the water twist. For that purpose it was necessary that the carriage should be put up without the necessity of applying the hand to the fly-wheel. At first we used them completely self-acting in all the motions—the fly continuing to revolve, and after receiving the full quantity of twist, the spindles stood—the guide or faller was turned down on the inside of the spindles, and the points were cleared of the thread at the same instant, by the rising of a guide, or inside faller, (if it might be so called.) When the outside guide-wire, or faller, was moved round, or turned down to a certain point on the inside of the spindles, it then disengaged, or rather allowed a pully, driven from the back of the belt pully, to come into gear or action, and which gave motion to the spindles, and took in the carriage at the same time, (similar to the way you assist the large mules in putting up).

But in the above self-acting mule, which performed every motion, after the spindles were stopped it required about three turns of the fly-wheel to move round the faller, and put in action the above-mentioned pully, that took in the carriage; which was a great loss of time. We therefore set aside that part of the apparatus or machinery, and allowed the mule to stop in the common way on receiving the full complement of twist; and the instant it stopped, the boy or girl, without putting their hand to the fly-wheel, just turned the guide or faller with the hand, which instantly set in motion the spindles, and took in the carriage—the cop being shaped by an inclined plane, or other contrivance.

It will naturally be asked, why were not the self-acting mules continued in use. At first, you know, the mules were about 144 spindles in size, and when power was applied, the spinner worked two of such; but the size of the mules rapidly increased to 300 spindles and upwards, and two such wheels being considered a sufficient task for a man to manage, the idea of saving by spinning with boys and girls was thus superseded.

Reading between the lines one can see that, although promising, Kelly's self-actor was not really good enough.

Other inventors followed Kelly in ever-increasing numbers until there was a virtual spate of self-actors patented between 1800 and 1830. During this period inventors were active in England, Scotland, France and America: but few were 'put into operation beyond the purposes of mere experiment' as James Montgomery, a Scottish spinner, wrote in 1833. Among those who had some success were

William Eaton of Derbyshire, Maurice de Jongh of Warrington, Mr Buchanan of Catrine Mills, Scotland, Mr Smith of Deanston, near Glasgow and Dr Brewster in America.

Self-actors of Eaton's pattern were installed in Manchester and France as well as in Derbyshire. Montgomery records that the Manchester mules did not give complete satisfaction and were dismantled; those in France proved a total failure, but those in Derbyshire were kept in use for almost twenty years. DeJongh installed twelve of his self-actors in a Warrington mill but did not persist with their use. Buchanan kept his mules in operation in his own mill but did not disclose their principle. It is unlikely that they were completely satisfactory. Smith joined forces with a Mr Robertson of Crofthead Mills, Renfrew to produce the Deanston Self-acting Mule and a few of these were built and operated in Scotland in 1830.

The sort of mechanism favoured by these inventors is typified by Eaton's backing-off motion and faller motion shown in Figs 8 and 9. John Platt, of Platt Bros the textile machinery makers, described how these motions worked in the *Proceedings of the Institution of Mechanical Engineers*, 1866:

> The main shaft or 'rim shaft' A, from which the driving motion of the spindles in the travelling carriage is derived, is itself driven in the forward direction during the twisting, and again during the winding, by the driving strap running on the fast pulley B, as shown by the dotted lines in Fig 8. The loose pulley C communicates a slow motion through intermediate pinions to the wheel D revolving loose upon the shaft A but in the contrary direction; and at the other end of the shaft A is a corresponding wheel E fast upon the shaft. The two toothed sectors FF are keyed upon a shaft G, which is carried in the rocking frame H; and the weight K on the rocking frame is constantly acting to draw the sectors back, out of gear with the wheels D and E; while the sectors themselves are only partly counterbalanced by the weight L, and are ready to fall down into gear with the wheels as soon as the catch I, by which they are held up out of gear is released. When the twisting of the threads is completed, the driving strap is shifted to the loose pulley C, and the forward motion remaining in the shaft A is arrested by a friction brake carrying a ratchet wheel, which is caught by a hook falling into gear at the moment of reversing the strap. The pull upon this

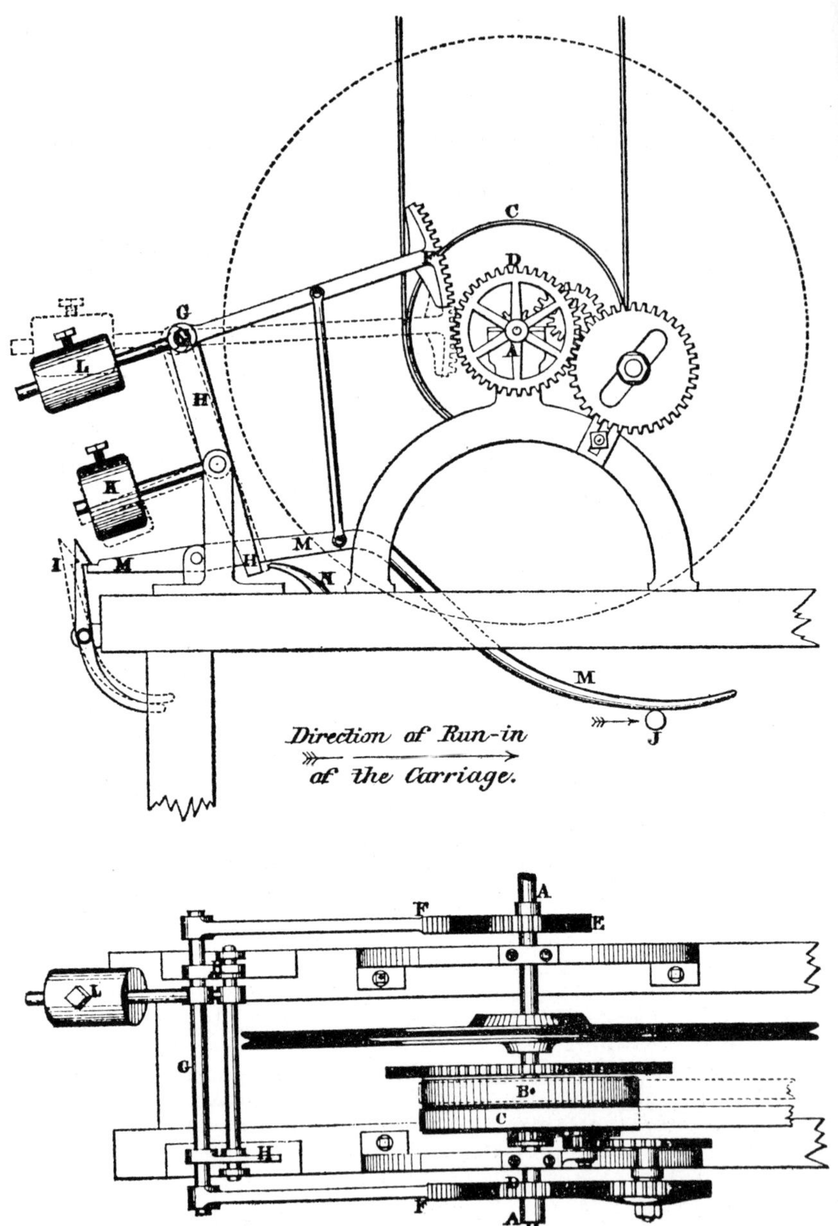

Fig 8. Eaton's backing-off motion of 1818

hook extends a spiral spring, the recoil of which is made to release the catch I; and the sectors F falling into gear with the wheels D and E, a backward motion is then communicated to the shaft A from the loose pulley C running forwards, whereby the spindles are made to turn backwards through the few revolutions necessary for backing off the spiral coils of thread at the top of the spindles, preparatory to winding. As the form of cop employed was a simple cone, increasing in height at the same time as in diameter (as shown in Fig 9), the length of the spiral coils that require backing-off at the top of the spindles becomes less with the increasing height of the cops on the spindles, and the number of backward turns in the backing-off has therefore to be gradually diminished as the cops approach completion; this is effected by an adjustable stop underneath the sectors F, which is gradually elevated in proportion to the increasing height of the cops. This stop is connected with a lever catching against a stud at the lower extremity of the arm H of the rocking frame; and the downward movement of the sectors F, while in gear with the wheels D and E, depresses the stop until at length the arm H is liberated; the weight K then withdraws the sectors out of gear, whereby the backward motion of the shaft A is stopped. By then shifting the driving strap to the fast pulley B, the shaft A is again driven in the forward direction, and the threads previously spun are wound up on the spindles as the carriage runs inwards. The pin J fixed upon the carriage, travelling inwards in the direction of the arrow, now comes in contact with the tail of the lever M, and lifts the sectors up again into their highest position, in which they are retained as before by the catch I at the other end of the lever M; and when the run-in of the carriage is nearly completed, the same pin J comes in contact with the tail of a second lever N. bearing against the extremity of the arm H of the rocking frame, whereby the sectors are thrown forwards again in readiness for the next time of backing-off.

Eaton's Faller Motion was almost identical with that in use at the present time, the difference being that the faller wire A was depressed by a weight B, instead of as in the present mules by a chain passing round a pulley upon the faller shaft C. The direction of the run-in of the carriage D carrying the spindles and cops E is shown by the arrows; and during the run-out in the opposite direction the weight B is held up in the position shown, by the catch F holding the tail of the lever G. This catch is withdrawn by the downward movement of the sectors in the backing-off motion, and the weight B then brings the front end of the lever G down upon an arm on the front side of the faller

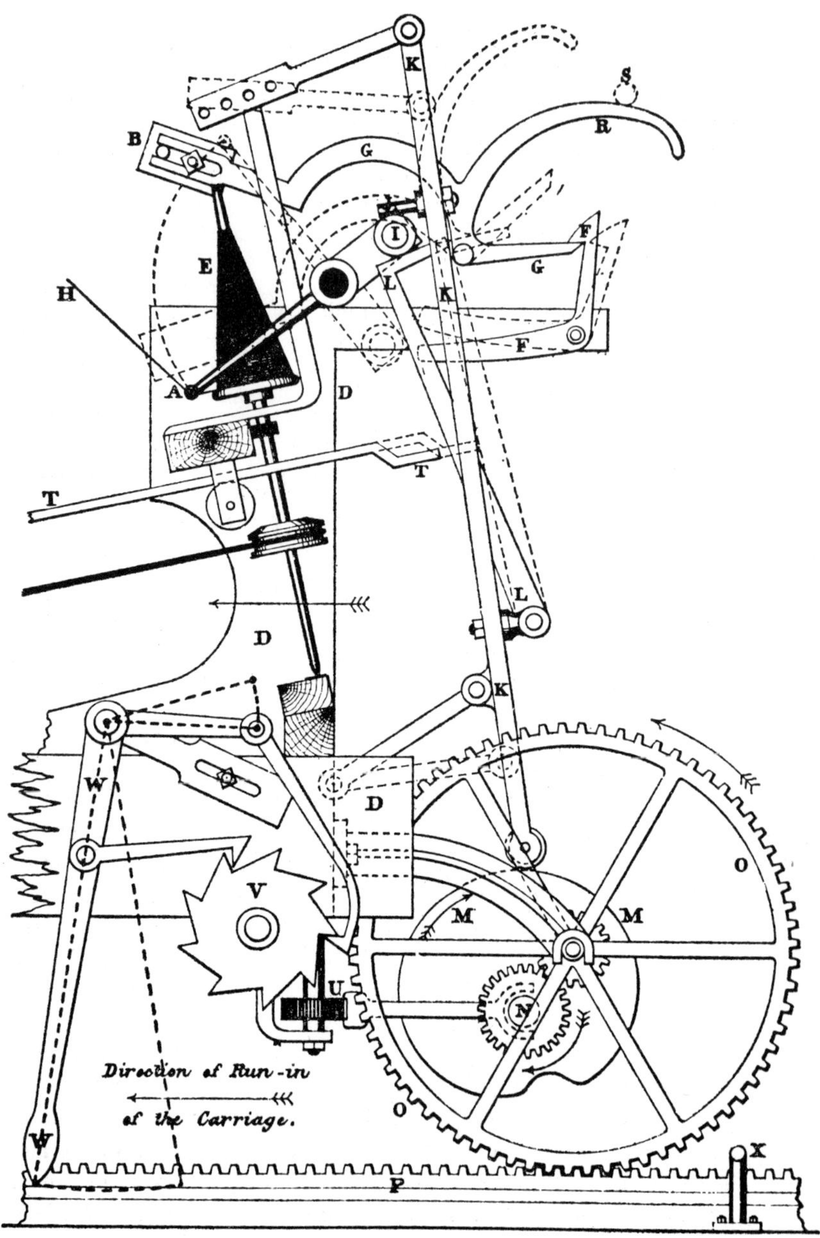

Fig 9. Eaton's faller motion of 1818

shaft C, depressing the faller wire A upon the threads H. The roller I, carried upon an arm on the back of the faller shaft, is thus brought up against the pin J fixed in the parallel-motion bar K, and is 'locked' by the latch L; so that by the vertical movement of the bar K the faller wire A is raised and lowered during the winding of the threads, for guiding them upon the cops from end to end. The reciprocation of the bar K is obtained by its bottom end resting upon the shaper fusee or long tapered cam M, which is driven by the pinion N from the toothed wheel O travelling along a rack P fixed upon the floor. As soon as the carriage has begun to run in, the weight B is lifted off the faller and raised again to its original position by the tail R of the lever coming in contact with a fixed stop S. When the carriage arrives at the end of its run-in, the sliding-bolt T coming against a fixed stop pushes back the latch L, and unlocks the roller I; and a balance weight upon the back of the faller shaft C raises the faller wire A clear of the threads into the extreme position shown by the dotted lines. For regulating the shape of the cop as its size increases, the shaper fusee M is gradually traversed endways along its shaft N by the rack and pinion U driven by a worm wheel from the ratchet V, which is turned round one tooth at a time by the lever W coming against a stop X fixed on the floor at each end of the run of the carriage.

If genius is defined as an infinite capacity for taking pains, such motions were works of genius: but something more than genius was needed. It required someone who could bring as much flair to the invention of a self-actor as Crompton himself had shown in the invention of the mule. Richard Roberts, a Manchester mill-wright, proved to be such a man. He was born in Llanymynech, Montgomery in 1789. As a boy he showed remarkable aptitude for making a superlative job of anything he set his hand to, and before he was out of his teens had established a considerable reputation as a mechanic and craftsman in his home district.

After spending some years in London in marine and machine-tool engineering, at the famous establishment of Maudsley & Co, Roberts went to Manchester and there, in 1816, at the age of twenty-seven set up in business for himself as a mill-wright and mechanic. He was joined a few years later by Thomas Sharpe, a business man who provided funds to complement Roberts' skill. In Manchester Roberts continued to add to his reputation as a successful and prolific inventor by making the first metal planing machine (now in the Science Museum) and designing the back-geared lathe headstock which was to be almost universally employed for more than a century.

The initiative in the design of the self-actor did not come from Roberts himself, who was extremely busy with his many interests. Although he had contributed greatly to the development of the power loom he did not regard himself as primarily a maker of textile machinery and, at first, paid little heed to requests that he apply himself to the design of an automatic mule. Early attempts to produce such a machine had risen largely from the enthusiasm of inventive minds interested in innovation almost for its own sake. By 1825, however, the situation had greatly changed and many mill owners were seeing self-actors as an imperative need rather than an inventor's plaything.

During the great industrial changes of the eighteenth century, trade unions were not illegal. From time to time Parliament passed laws regulating employment and procedures for fixing wage rates in specific industries. Combinations of workmen to secure enforcement of these laws were allowed and petitions from such combinations were frequently accepted by Parliament, but towards the end of the century, on various pretexts, laws began to be passed forbidding combinations in particular trades. Then in 1799, after judges had declared trade unions to be illegal in common law, the first Combinations Act, forbidding all trade unions, was passed. The Act was slightly amended in 1800 but remained an extremely harsh measure, prescribing three months in jail or three months' hard labour for any working man who joined with another to gain an increase in wages or a decrease in hours. The sentence was to be given by two magistrates and no appeal was allowed, except under circumstances which effectively barred it to working men.

Unions continued to exist in the form of friendly societies, but they could do little to smooth out the difficulties which inevitably arose in an industry which was expanding rapidly and subject to many technical changes. Their ineffectiveness was ensured by such rigid application of the combination laws as occurred at Bolton in 1818. Two secretaries and the president of a union who had called and attended a meeting at the request of the employers were found guilty of conspiracy and sentenced to two years' and one year's imprisonment respectively. This sort of action bred a deep resentment and distrust on the part of the unions, so that the repeal of the combination laws in 1824 brought an explosive reaction.

The years of frustration had hardened the working man's attitude towards labour-saving innovations and, in the spinning industry, towards the use of very long mules in particular. Additionally, Nassau Senior, the government commissioner reporting on trade unions in the industry, c 1830, believed that spinners were further encouraged in this attitude and incited to action by industrialists with older machinery who were anxious to prevent their rivals installing new and better machines.

Whatever the causes, the immediate outcome of the repeal of the combination laws was a widespread and very determined spinners' strike, which led a consortium of mill owners to approach Roberts and persuade him to apply his ingenuity to the mule. In choosing Roberts the mill owners had chosen well. He appears to have taken the challenge in his stride, applying for his first patent the following year and virtually completing the task by 1830. His design of that year discloses a plan which found wide acceptance at the time and established the basic principles on which self-actors were to be built for more than a century. Just how quickly Roberts' mule found acceptance is indicated by an account written by James Montgomery barely three years later.

> Mr Roberts has constructed a self-acting mule, which is admitted by all who have had fair opportunities of witnessing its merits, to exceed their most sanguine expectations. It is one of the most beautiful specimens of mechanical combination that is to be found; exhibiting a rare degree of original invention, highly creditable to the ingenuity and perseverance of the inventor. For although but a short time since its completion there are now self-acting mule spindles in operation to the extent of 100,000 spindles and orders to the amount of 120,000 more are just now (June 1833) in course of execution.

That a Scottish spinner in close contact with Lanarkshire development of the Deanston mule should be so enthusiastic is a most convincing testimony to Roberts' invention.

Montgomery also noted that a material advantage of Roberts' invention was that a common hand mule could easily be made self-acting at small expense, requiring only the self-acting headstock and the fitting of a counterfaller. This may well have been a material advantage to Montgomery and his fellow spinners, but it did little to repay the development costs incurred by Sharpe, Roberts & Co. Although enthusiasm for the new mule continued to grow (more than 500,000 spindles were in use by 1837) the return to the inventor was so inadequate that Parliament was petitioned for an extension of the patent. Sharpe, Roberts & Co had spent £12,000 on the developments covered by the 1830 patent but by 1839 had recovered only £7,000 in profits—less than 3d per spindle. In the event the patent was extended for a further seven years but it is unlikely that the total return over the whole period was even a fair return for the original investment. There was certainly no pecuniary reward for Roberts' genius.

In 1843, three years before completion of the extended period of the patent, the partnership between Sharpe and Roberts was ended. The firm continued as Richard Roberts & Co and became famous as locomotive builders, but did not prosper. No doubt Roberts' versatility and breadth of interest was a considerable handicap to the company. While other firms became great by specialising in the manufacture of textile machinery, Roberts took on all kinds of interesting work such as the invention, design and manufacture in 1847 of the heavy plate-punching machines used to make the rivet holes in the Britannia tubular bridge built over the Menai Straits by Robert Stephenson.

By this time at least a score of machinery makers were building their own versions of the Roberts self-actor and some of them were improving greatly on the original. Roberts himself moved to other things and in 1852 wound up his business in Manchester and went to live in London. There he practised as a consultant, devoting himself almost exclusively to invention. He died in poverty in 1864. The Government subsequently granted his daughter an annuity of £300 in recognition of Roberts' services to industry. In the matter of reward for his inventive genius it would appear that Roberts fared no better than did Crompton, despite the fact that he took out adequate patents and made business-like arrangements for the manufacture and sale of his invention. He did, however, have the satisfaction of seeing the self-actor succeed in the way he intended. While poor Crompton grieved that what he had devised as an aid to domestic industry became one of the most formidable monsters of the new factory age, Roberts was proud that his brainchild grew to become perhaps the most admired mechanical prodigy of the day.

5

The Mechanism of the Self-actor

DURING the early nineteenth century it was popular to describe as 'self-acting' any machine which, in the language of today, would be called automatic. Then, as now, the term was to a large extent comparative, in that no machine can be completely self-acting or completely automatic. To Crompton the steam-driven mule jennies of 1820 must have seemed self-acting. After all, these mules spun about 300 5 ft lengths of yarn simultaneously and completely automatically, relating the draft, twist, ratch and final twisting precisely by means of pre-set gearing. It remained only for the spinner to wind up the lengths of yarn, on completion of which task the machine would automatically recommence spinning.

Self-acting meant very much more to Roberts. He designed his machine so that it would spin and wind each draw automatically. In addition it would automatically make the necessary adjustments between successive draws to take account of the growing size of the cop and the decreasing length of bare spindle blade, from commencing to spin on a bare spindle to completion of the cop. In the event, this proved to be rather more than was at first called for and it was almost fifty years before his ingenious design was fully utilised.

The working elements of a self-actor of the Roberts pattern had a great deal in common with those of the ordinary manually controlled jenny: as Montgomery had observed, common jennies could be easily converted to self-actors. Indeed, if Figs 10 and 6 are

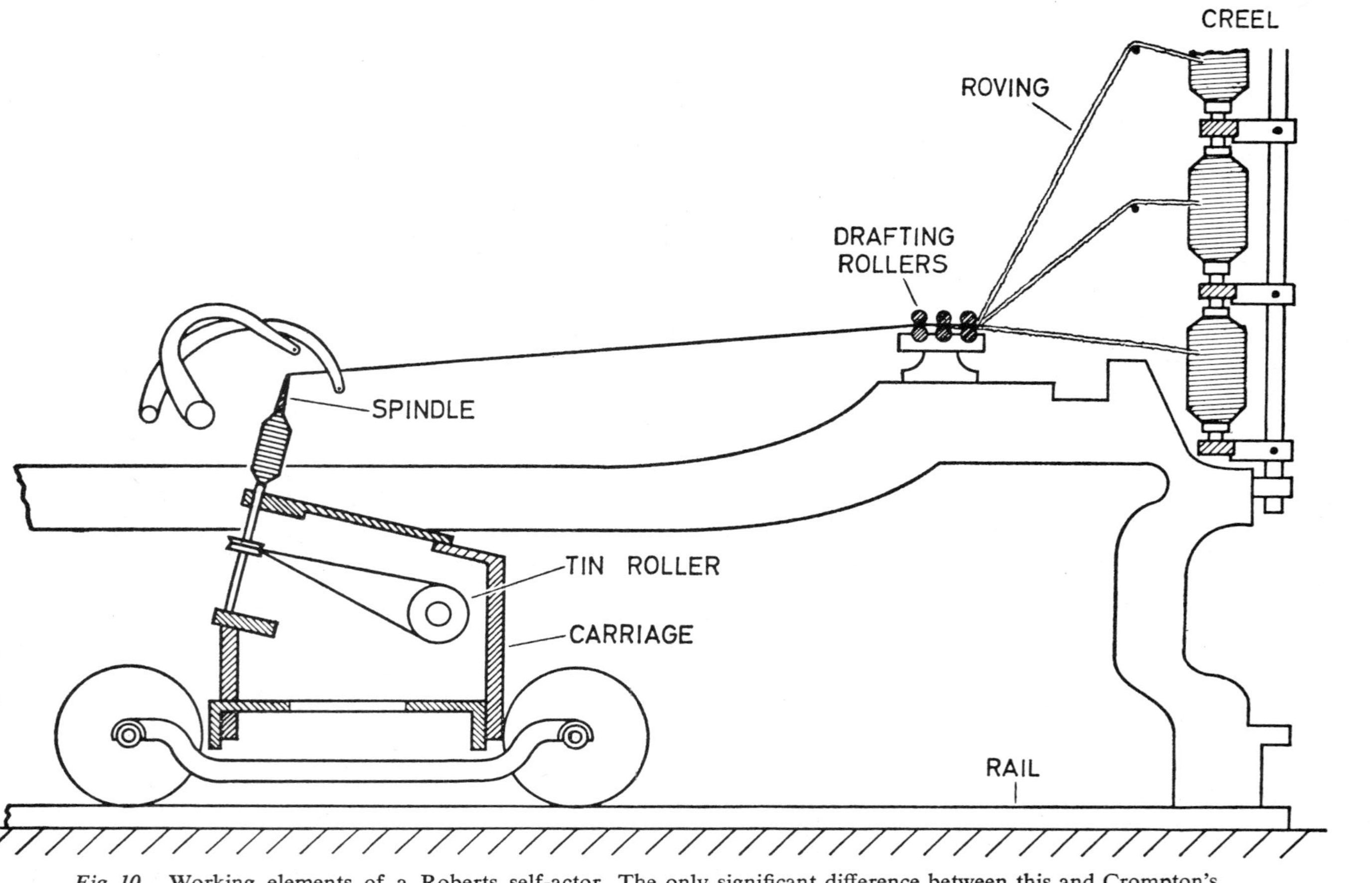

Fig 10. Working elements of a Roberts self-actor. The only significant difference between this and Crompton's

compared, it will be seen that the working elements had changed little since Crompton first established the process of mule spinning. The most important alteration from the yarn quality point of view was the use of three lines of drafting rollers where Crompton had only two. This was not a development exclusive to the mule but was shared with the water frame and throstle, where it had been found that three lines gave more uniform drafting than could be obtained with two. Usually a break draft of about 1·5 between the back and middle rollers was followed by a main draft, variable between 4 and 8, giving an overall draft of from 6 to 12. Each line of rollers comprised a continuous iron roller, finely fluted longitudinally and supported at 12 to 20 in intervals by bronze-lined half bearings bolted to the cast-iron roller beam, on to which the upper line of resiliently clad rollers were pressed. These top rollers were always arranged as pairs of 'bosses'. For the finest counts the bosses were short and each drafted only one end of roving. For coarse yarn it was regarded as satisfactory to have three or even four ends to a boss. The mule shown on page 133 is spinning coarse yarn and it can be seen from the way they are grouped that there are four ends to each boss. The pairs of bosses were usually pressed into contact with the bottom roller by a system of saddles loaded by a single lever, as shown in Fig 11.

With all drafting systems the accuracy and resilience of the top rollers vitally affects the quality of drafting. Today specially formulated compounds of synthetic rubber and granulated cork are used, but in the nineteenth century these were not available. Instead, the art of clothing rollers with a specially woven wool flannel within a sheath of thin goat or sheep skin was highly developed. Roller coverers became incredibly skilled in the making of scarfed joints so precise that the clothed rollers were, and remained, cylindrically true to within about 0·0015 in.

The other important change was introduced by Roberts. The faller, a taut steel wire extending the length of the carriage, was supplemented in the self-actor by a counterfaller. During the draw both wires were locked clear of the yarn, the faller wire about 1 in above and the counterfaller about 1 in below the yarn sheet. During backing-off the faller was depressed to contact the yarn and guide it throughout the subsequent winding, much as on a common jenny. Meanwhile the counterfaller was released and allowed to lift, under the action of springs or weights, so as to take up the slack in the yarn sheet and apply tension to the yarn during winding.

The construction of the carriage and the mounting of the spindles remained unchanged. The carriage was generally made of mahogany and supported on iron bearers, carried on double-flanged iron

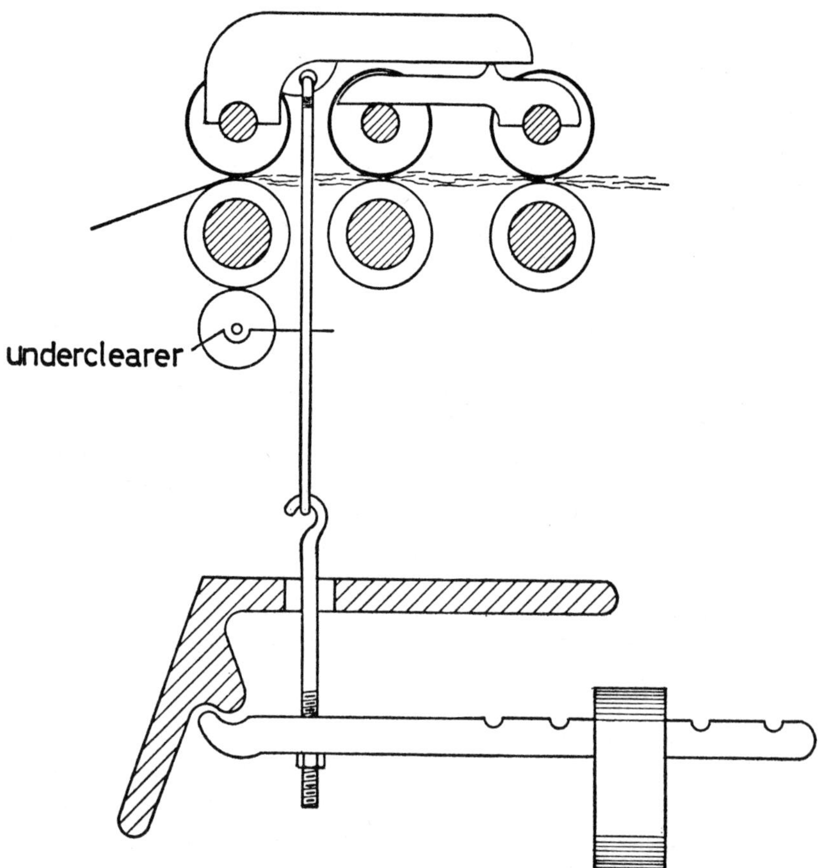

Fig 11. Oldham-style drafting rollers. The upper three rollers, which were covered with leather, were driven by frictional contact with the positively driven, fluted iron bottom rollers

wheels, at intervals of 8 or 10 ft along its length. The wheels ran on accurately positioned edge rails secured to the floor of the spinning room. The spindles had an overall length of about 14 in and were made of hardened steel. About $\frac{5}{16}$ in in diameter in the middle, each spindle tapered to about $\frac{1}{8}$ in diameter at its lower end, which was conically pointed to run in a bronze footstep bearing. A second bearing consisting of a plain bronze sleeve was provided immediately above the wharf (or driving pulley). Above this upper bearing the spindle tapered upwards to a smoothly rounded tip about $\frac{1}{10}$ in in diameter.

Although the working elements themselves had changed very little, the means by which they were driven and controlled were very different in the self-actor. Some of the differences can be seen by comparing Fig 7 and Fig 12, but for a full appreciation of the mechanism of the self-actor it is necessary to consider the driving arrangements to the various machine elements individually. Some remain essentially the same as in the manually controlled mule, others were completely different and all were refined and developed as mules became larger and ran faster.

At first either drums or rollers were used to drive the spindles. Drums were broad flat pulleys mounted with their axes parallel to the spindles. Each drum drove two dozen or so spindles by means of as many light driving bands. In the early machines the drums were driven, one from another along the whole length of the carriage, by heavier bands running in V-grooved pulleys. Later a single shaft running the whole length of the carriage drove each drum individually through bevel gearing.

The use of rollers gave a simpler layout of the carriage. Only one roller was needed for each mule. It was built up in sections and was mounted with its axis of rotation along the length of the carriage, that is, parallel to the drafting rollers and at right angles to the spindles. This meant, of course, that the path of each driving band did not lie in one plane and it might be thought that at least one additional guiding pulley would have been needed. In practice, however, it was found that light bands, sufficient for the task, ran quite satisfactorily without guides. In the early days some difficulty was experienced with the weight and inertia of the rollers. Had

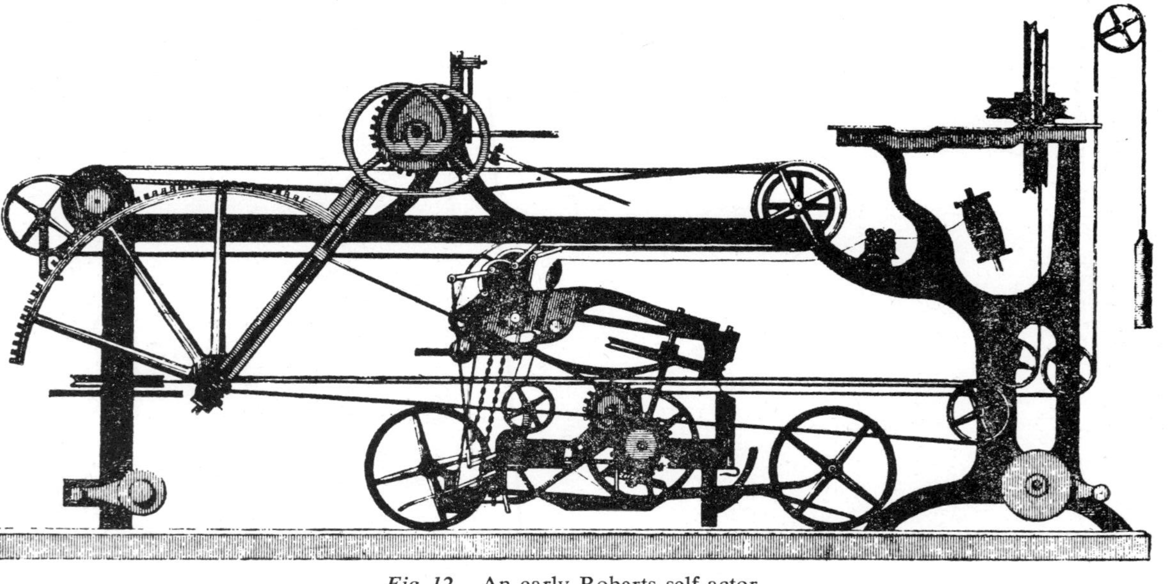

Fig 12. An early Roberts self-actor

the spindles run steadily at a constant speed this would not have mattered a great deal, but under the conditions of mule spinning, where spindles are accelerated to a very high speed, stopped, briefly reversed and finally run at a precisely varying speed during winding, unduly high inertia could not be tolerated. Fortunately the craftsmen of the day were equal to the challenge. They devised means by which the rollers were built up, in 6 to 8 ft lengths, from small sheets of thin tinplate soldered together to form a very light, yet surprisingly rigid, roller. The construction of tin rollers was a most impressive example of the tinsmith's craft. Not only was it necessary for the rollers to be truly cylindrical but it was also necessary for dynamic balance of the sections to be achieved.

The rival claims of drums and rollers were keenly contested for many years. Writing in 1893, Thomas Thornley, in 'A practical treatise upon self-acting mules', admitted that tin rollers had nearly driven drums out of the trade. However, he lamented that, although rather more noisy, 'drums ran much lighter in motion than tin rollers'. Despite Thornley's nostalgia, drums gave way entirely to tin rollers and in later mules the tin rollers were so well balanced that lengths of more than 120 ft ran very sweetly at speeds as high as 1,000 rpm.

In early mules the rim shaft was mounted parallel to the rollers and the carriage and was placed in a position convenient for manual putting-up. With self-actors there was no such constraint on the position of the rim, and it became usual to place the shaft horizontally, at right angles to the rollers and the carriage. The rim pulley itself was secured to the end of the shaft, behind the headstock and outside the bearings, where it could be used as a change point for determination of the spindle speed. The tin roller (or drum) shaft was driven from the rim by means of the rim band, a single endless rope passing round a system of guide pulleys which permitted movement of the carriage without variation of the band tension. The usual arrangement is shown in Fig 13. On large mules the pulleys were all triple-grooved and the rim band itself was about 100 ft long and $\frac{5}{8}$ in in diameter. Both the rim pulley and the tin roller shaft pulley rotated in truly vertical planes: but the mountings of the guide pulleys were cunningly angled so that the

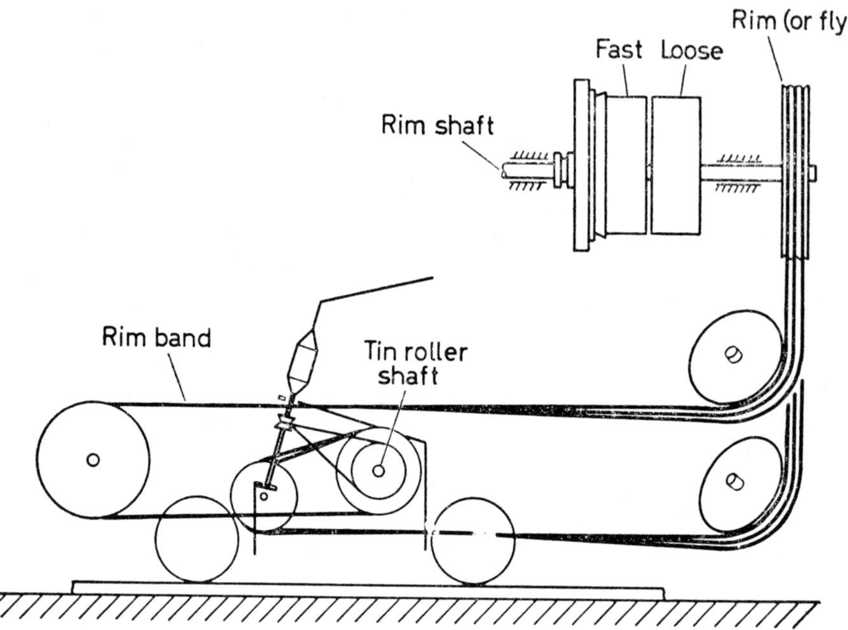

Fig. 13. Drive to spindles when spinning. Onc endless rim band passed three times round the system of pulleys to make a triple band drive

band remained in the grooves during both forward and backward rotation, yet followed an endless path to embrace all three grooves in turn.

The drive to the rim shaft was not materially changed. The well-established arrangement of a continuously rotating countershaft, coupled to the rim by a flat belt and a pair of fast and loose pulleys, was as well suited to the needs of the self-actor as it had been to the common mule jenny. On completion of the draw and, where necessary, twisting at the head, power to the rim and spindles was withdrawn by moving the belt onto the loose pulley as on manually controlled mules. At this point a contra-rotating member, commonly a conical friction clutch known as the backing-off friction, was engaged to bring the rim shaft to rest and then rotate it in the opposite direction. As the spindles turned backwards the winding faller was pulled down and the counterfaller allowed to rise and take up the resulting slack in the yarn sheet. Backing-off proceeded until the winding faller had been brought down level with the tip of the cop, at which point the backing-off friction was disengaged and the rim shaft and spindles were left completely free.

The greatest problem in the development of the self-actor was the driving of the spindles during winding. It had defeated all earlier attempts to achieve completely automatic action and it was here that Roberts made his most decisive contribution. The kernel of the difficulty lay in the disparity between the sheer brute power needed to accelerate the spindles and cops to their working speed in the shortest possible time, and the delicate precision needed to back-off and wind on the yarn without having either a surplus or a deficiency at the end of the inward run of the carriage.

Crompton had used the fly or rimshaft to drive the spindles at all times. Kelly had arranged to supply power to the rim shaft during spinning, but left it free to be manually rotated during backing-off and winding. There were many attempts to apply power through the rim shaft during winding, but none was successful. Satisfactory all-powered working was achieved only when Roberts devised a winding system which was completely independent of the rim shaft. He had appreciated that the rim and rim band method of coupling, although ideal for rapid acceleration and sustained high speed rotation of the spindles, left a great deal to be desired where precise control of relatively low-speed rotation was concerned.

The problems in winding were extremely complex. They stemmed largely from the fact that the preferred form of yarn package was the cop or cope. This is a package of considerable antiquity, developed in the days of spinning with the simple spindle and whorl. The Saxony wheel, and later Arkwright's water frame, could not make the traditional cop and were usually arranged to produce a flanged spool or bobbin. This was never popular but was tolerated as a clumsy and inconvenient substitute for a cop. The cop has two very important advantages: firstly, because it needs no central core or bobbin it is both light and compact.

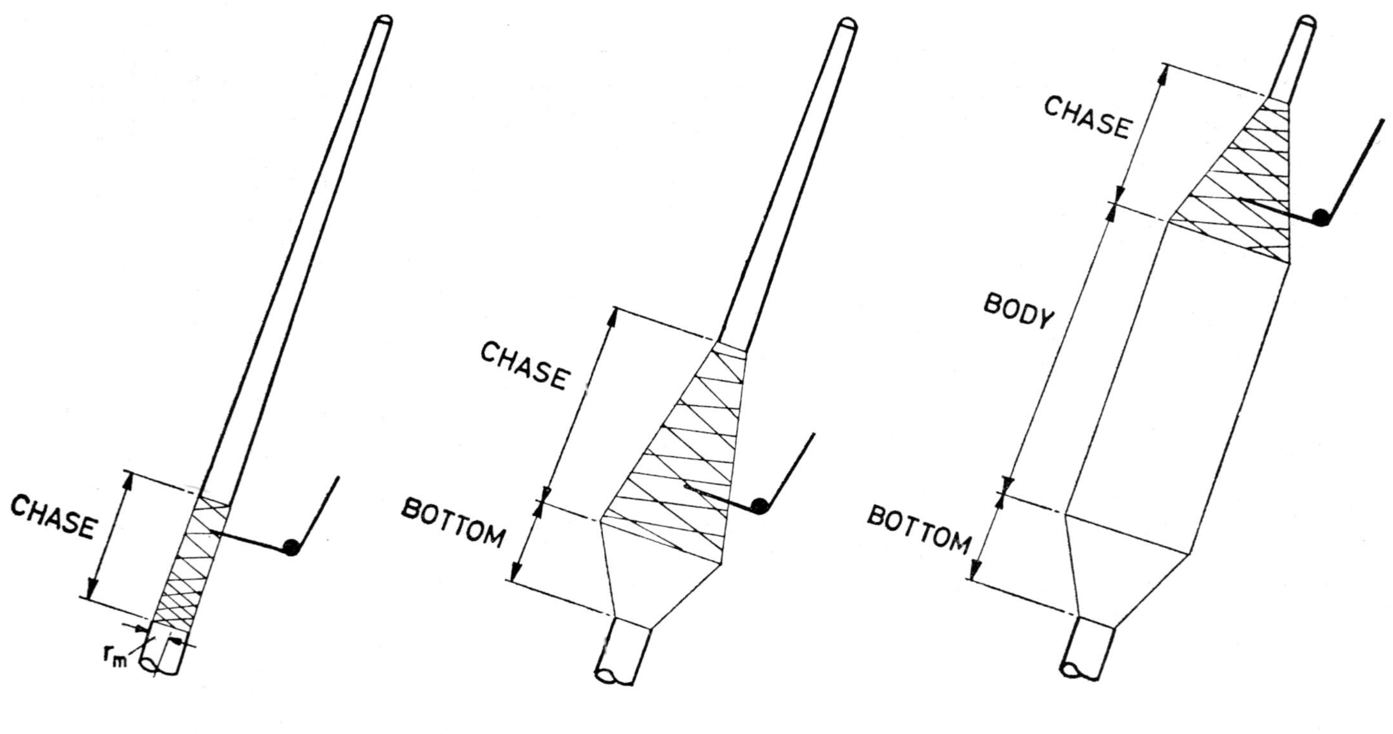

Fig 14. Stages in cop formation. Winding only on the chase, the upper conical surface, ensured that the yarn could be drawn-off axially during weaving without rotating the cop

Secondly, and perhaps most important, it does not have to be rotated for the finest yarn to be withdrawn over-end at very high speeds.

Cops were formed on the mule exactly as they had been formed by hand spinners and jenny spinners. The first draws were wound directly onto the bare, tapered spindle just above the whorl or driving wharf. The yarn was so disposed in each layer as continuously to increase the angle of taper of the surface on which winding took place without ever winding below the point of maximum diameter. This proceeded until the required final package diameter was reached. Thereafter the length of the package was progressively increased, while maintaining a constant maximum diameter and with only minor changes in the angle of the conical winding surface. The winding surface was called the chase, and in winding up each draw it was traversed quickly in the downwards direction and slowly in the upwards direction. This construction, illustrated in Fig 14, gives a package of considerable mechanical strength and permits free unwinding from the chase. Before the introduction of the pirn-changing automatic loom, the mule cop was unrivalled as a shuttle package.

The spindle-rotation requirements for satisfactory winding of such a package on a mule may be summarised by saying that, ideally, the spindle speed should at all times be directly proportional to the inward speed of the carriage and inversely proportional to the diameter of the chase at the point at which winding is taking place. In addition there is the important, overriding requirement that the total length of yarn wound during each and every run-in must be exactly equal to the length of the draw. To meet these requirements Roberts evolved his ingenious quadrant mechanism (Fig 15) and his equally ingenious system of closed-loop automatic control. A most important feature of the mechanism was the fact that, for the first time, carriage movement and spindle rotation were directly related.

The spindles were driven by the unwinding of a chain wrapped round a drum geared to the tin roller (or drum) shaft, the other end of the chain being attached to a point on the quadrant arm. The point of attachment was a nut located in guides provided by

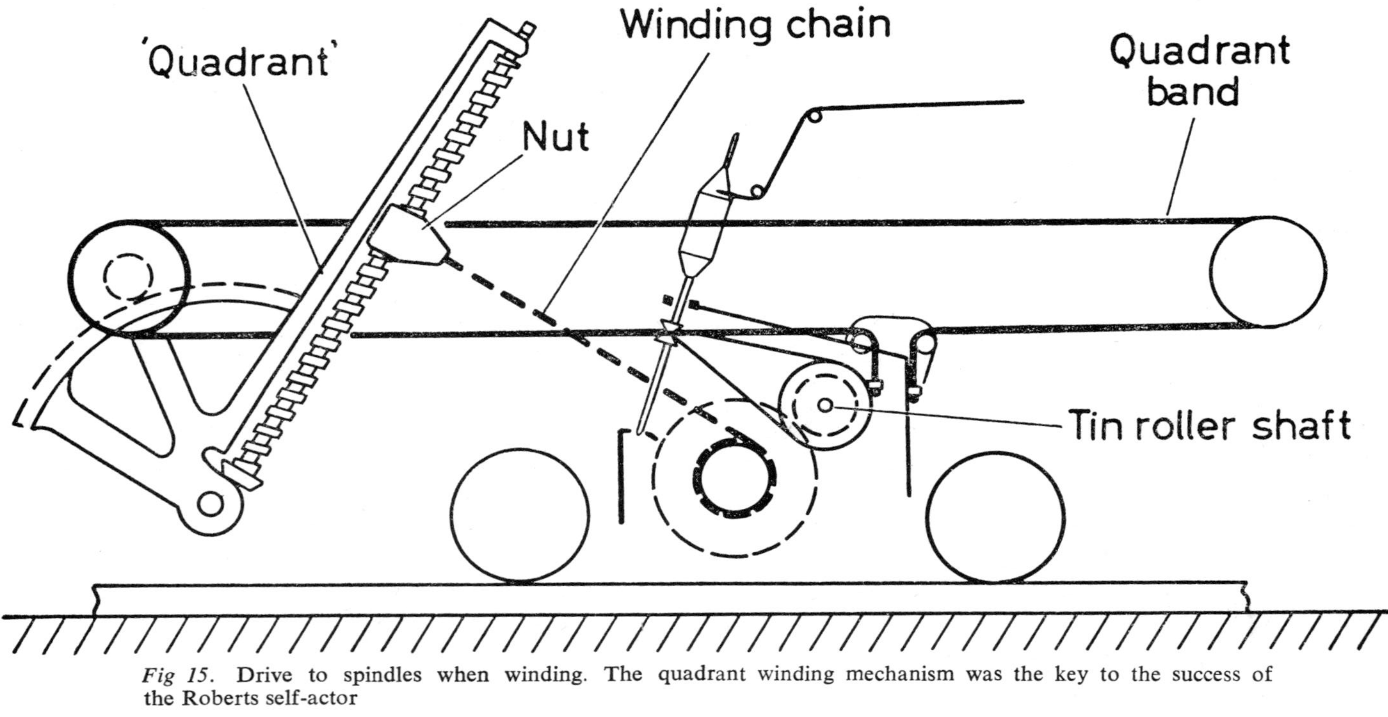

Fig 15. Drive to spindles when winding. The quadrant winding mechanism was the key to the success of the Roberts self-actor

the quadrant arm and positioned radially by a strong screw extending the whole length of the arm. The quadrant itself was driven from the movement of the carriage in such a way that its angular velocity was always proportional to the carriage speed. The spindle speed at any instant was proportional to the rate at which chain was unwound from the drum. This, in turn, depended upon the relative speed of the quadrant nut and the chain drum. The nut speed was varied by altering the position of the nut along the quadrant arm. As the diameter of the cop increased, the nut was moved out along the arm so that the amount of chain unwound from the drum, and thus the number of revolutions of the spindles, during a complete inwards run was progressively reduced.

The action is explained in Fig 16. In both diagrams the full line shows the position of the quadrant arm, chain and chain drum at the beginning of the inward run of the carriage; A and B indicate the point of attachment of the chain to the arm and the point at which the chain is leaving the surface of the drum. The broken line shows the positions of the same parts at the end of the inwards run, A_1, B_1 being the points on the chain then corresponding to the initial points A, B. Thus the length of chain unwound during the appropriate inwards run is the difference between the final length of free chain A_1, B_1 and the initial length A, B. It is clear that this difference (and hence the number of revolutions made by the drum and the spindles) is very much greater in the upper diagram, where the quadrant nut is very near to the fulcrum of the quadrant, than in the lower diagram where the nut is well out along the quadrant arm.

Thus this simple mechanism provided a ready, yet precise, means by which the number of turns made by the spindles during each inwards run could be progressively varied to take account of the increasing diameter of the cone as cop formation proceeded. It had, in addition, a delightful subtlety in that it also gave a variation of speed during each inward run to take account of the varying diameter onto which yarn was being wound, as the faller guided the yarn first in a rapid helix from apex to base of the chase and then in a slower helix back from the base to the apex.

A general appreciation of this feature can be gained by referring

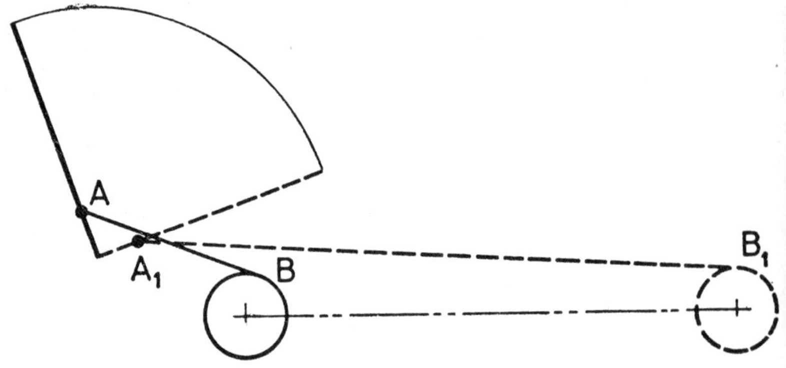

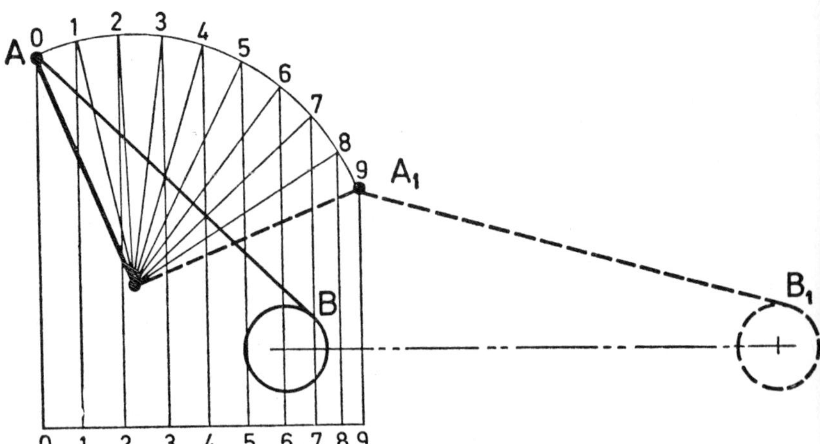

Fig 16. Action of the quadrant winding mechanism. The upper figure shows the position of the quadrant nut, A, at Stage 1 of cop formation (Fig 14). The lower figure shows the position of the nut during the period from Stage 2 to Stage 3

back to Fig 16. In the upper diagram the movement of the nut, A, is little, compared with the movement of the carriage, and under these conditions it is clear that the rate at which chain is being unwound is chiefly dependent on the rate of movement of the point B. Thus the speed of rotation of the spindles is roughly constant throughout the run-in. This is as it should be. This position of the quadrant nut gives the maximum number of spindle revolutions during the run-in and is the position used when winding the first layers of yarn onto the bare spindle. At this stage of cop formation the diameter onto which yarn is being wound is almost constant, and it is therefore an advantage that the spindle speed is almost directly proportional to the carriage speed during winding.

The position of the quadrant nut in the lower diagram gives the minimum number of spindle turns during the run-in and is the position used when the full diameter of the cop chase has been reached. Once this has happened, the diameter on which winding takes place at the beginning of the run-in is a minimum equal to the spindle-blade diameter at the apex of the chase, increases to a maximum equal to the full cop diameter during the first third of the inward run, and then reduces back to blade diameter on completion of the run-in. Thus it is desirable that the spindle speed should start high, fall to a minimum during the first third of the run-in, and then increase to a maximum at the end of the run.

Study of the lower diagram of Fig 16 will show that this characteristic is given by Roberts' ingenious mechanism. The points 0 to 9 marked on the arc described by the quadrant nut are at equal intervals of 10°. The points 0 to 9 projected onto the base line show the horizontal distances moved by the quadrant nuts. It is, of course, a part of a sinusoidal function and the horizontal velocity of the nut increases at first and then decreases as the run-in proceeds. It can be seen that the rate at which chain is unwound is, to a first approximation, proportional to the difference between the speed of the carriage and the horizontal component of the speed of the quadrant nut. As this relative speed at first decreases, then increases smoothly to reach a maximum at the end of the inward run, the pattern of behaviour meets the general requirements of the situation very nicely.

This superficial description of the action does no more than show that the Roberts winding mechanism roughly met the requirements. A rigid analytical treatment would be out of place here, but such an examination has shown that the mechanism does in fact meet the requirements very precisely indeed. Roberts had devised a most ingenious mechanism, and had also proportioned its components so well that almost perfect winding could be obtained at all stages of cop formation.

It was, of course, necessary for the quadrant nut to be moved out along the quadrant arm as the diameter of the cop increased, and the number of spindle turns needed to wind up one draw was correspondingly reduced. Failure to move the nut out as the cop diameter increased was serious, in that it caused more yarn to be wound than had been spun in the preceding draw. As a result there was not enough yarn available to form the spindle blade coils and to reach from the tip of the spindles to the rollers during laying-on. At first a very small error could be taken up by the elasticity of the yarn, but as the error increased nicking of the yarn began to occur, that is, the yarn began to fail, partly by breakage of the fibres and partly by slippage, at a point at which a nick or neck began to develop. Such nicks were troublesome to the weaver, particularly in warp yarns. If an even larger error were allowed to develop the result was a sawney—the disastrous breakage of all the ends as the mule let-in.

On the other hand, if the quadrant nut were moved out too far, not enough yarn would be wound on and there would be more than sufficient available for laying-on. This too was bad because on completion of laying-on the excess yarn formed a snarl. Small snarls were pulled out during the subsequent draw and little harm was done: but bigger snarls became locked in the yarn and caused trouble to the weaver. In practice it was usual to maintain a nut setting so that the length wound during each run-in was a little less than the length of the draw, not so little as to result in locked snarls but enough for just a tiny snarl to form at let-in, as an assurance that the yarn was not being nicked.

The length of snarl which was permissible depended on the count being spun and the hardness of the twist. With very fine, hard-twisted yarns as little as ¼ in of yarn could form a locked snarl but with coarse weft yarns any snarls containing more than 1 in of yarn could be pulled out during the draw without leaving a trace. For the generality of yarns spun on the early self-actors it was perfectly acceptable to have up to ½ in of yarn surplus on completion of winding. This would briefly form a snarl of about ¼ in which was pulled out during the early part of the draw. Although care was needed to keep snarling within this limit by manual adjustment of the quadrant-nut position, it was by no means an exacting task compared with the operation of common mule jennies.

At the time of the introduction of the self-actor a typical mule spinning 80's yarn, whether manually controlled or self-acting, would have a cycle time of about twenty working hours from starting to wind on the bare spindle to completion of a set of cops. For the spinner on manually controlled mules this meant the strenuous operation of putting-up each of his pair of heavy mules some 2,400 times. His brother spinner working (or minding) a pair of self-actors had a much easier job. Winding for him involved only the adjustment of the position of the quadrant nut during the period in which the cop bottom was being formed. Once the full diameter of the cop had been reached the self-actor really was completely self-acting. Of the total of around 2,400 draws needed to build a full cop of 80's yarn, roughly 500 went to formation of the cop bottom. For the first few minutes after doffing the cop diameter increased very rapidly, and it was necessary to make an adjustment during almost every draw. This did not last long. As the cop diameter increased the rate of change of diameter was dramatically reduced, and the frequency with which adjustments were needed fell correspondingly. (This effect is readily appreciated by anyone who has wound a ball of wool by hand. The ball grows very rapidly at first.) As the cop bottom approached completion adjustment was needed only at intervals of twenty or so draws.

In the early days of the self-actor, completion of the cop bottom when spinning 80's yarn took a little over four hours, and for winding to proceed satisfactorily the minder of a self-actor had to make about ninety adjustments to the setting of the quadrant nut during this period. For the remaining sixteen hours of the set he could leave the mule mechanism to look after itself. Even during the four hours of adjustment it must have seemed an easy life to the ex-hand mule spinner, for the actual making of the adjustment was simplicity itself. A cranked handle was attached to the outer end of the quadrant screw and this could be turned readily and safely by hand as the mule was moving out. Once some familiarity had been gained it was not uncommon for the minder to station a small boy at the headstock and have him make the desired adjustments in response to agreed hand signals—one finger for a quarter-turn of the screw, two for a half-turn.

To the spinners of the day this must have seemed an incredible advance on the laborious hand mule, and a lesser man than Roberts would have been content to regard his task as finished. Roberts, however, was a perfectionist and he was not happy to leave control of the quadrant setting to the judgment of the spinner. He chose instead to complete his assignment by providing means by which this adjustment could be made completely automatically and very precisely. The device he used to make the adjustment was extremely ingenious. It was also of the greatest importance in that it embodied a new principle, that of error-actuated servo-control, which has since been widely developed as the basis of twentieth-century automatic control theory. This facet of the development of the mule, although complex, is of such interest and importance that it is treated separately in Chapter 6.

Driving the carriage and rollers during the outward run involved no special difficulties. Early mule carriages were drawn out by bands at the headstock only and kept parallel to the roller beam by squaring bands (fixed ropes passing over idling pulleys mounted on the ends of the carriage). As mules became longer it became the practice to supplement the squaring bands by a horizontal shaft, known as the back shaft, which ran the whole length of the mule parallel to, and behind, the roller beam. Helically grooved drums about 5 in in diameter were fixed at intervals along the back shaft. Ropes, attached to these drums and to the carriage, passed round guide pulleys in such a way as to permit both acceleration and deceleration of the carriage to be controlled by rotation of the back shaft. Gears and a dog clutch were used to drive the back shaft from the rim shaft during the outward run, and another dog clutch was used to take the drive to the front roller of the drafting system. A typical arrangement is shown in Fig 17.

The speed of the carriage during the outward run was severely limited by the practical consideration that the rate of draw had to be related to the speed of rotation of the spindles. When spinning 80's yarn, for example, it was necessary for the spindles to make about thirty-two revolutions during the time taken for the carriage to move out 1 in. In the early days of self-actors the maximum spindle speed was limited to about 4,000 rpm, permitting a carriage speed of up to 125 in per minute when spinning 80's yarn. Thus the duration of the outward run for a 60 in draw was approaching thirty seconds. During the inward run the carriage speed was not limited in this way. Even when winding on the bare spindle only about fifty spindle turns were needed for the whole of the run-in. It became the practice, therefore, to provide separate driving means by which the carriage could be put-up very quickly indeed. The problem here was that of accelerating and decelerating the carriage itself. To do this four spiral drums, known as scrolls, were mounted on a very substantial shaft at the back of the headstock.

Fig 18 shows how two of the scrolls were arranged to draw the carriage in directly by means of two cotton bands, each about $1\frac{1}{2}$ in in diameter, while the other two scrolls were used to check the inward movement by means of similar bands passed round guide pulleys at the front of the headstock. The scrolls were so shaped as to give substantially constant acceleration during the first half of the run-in followed by substantially constant deceleration during the second half. Thus the carriage was smoothly accelerated to a maximum speed then equally smoothly brought to rest. During the run-in the scroll shaft was driven from a separate power source independent of the rim shaft. Flat belts and fast and loose pulleys were sometimes used but on later mules the most common arrangement was that shown in Fig 18. Here a separate rope drive from the countershaft, usually double or triple grooved and known as the taking-up band, was coupled to the

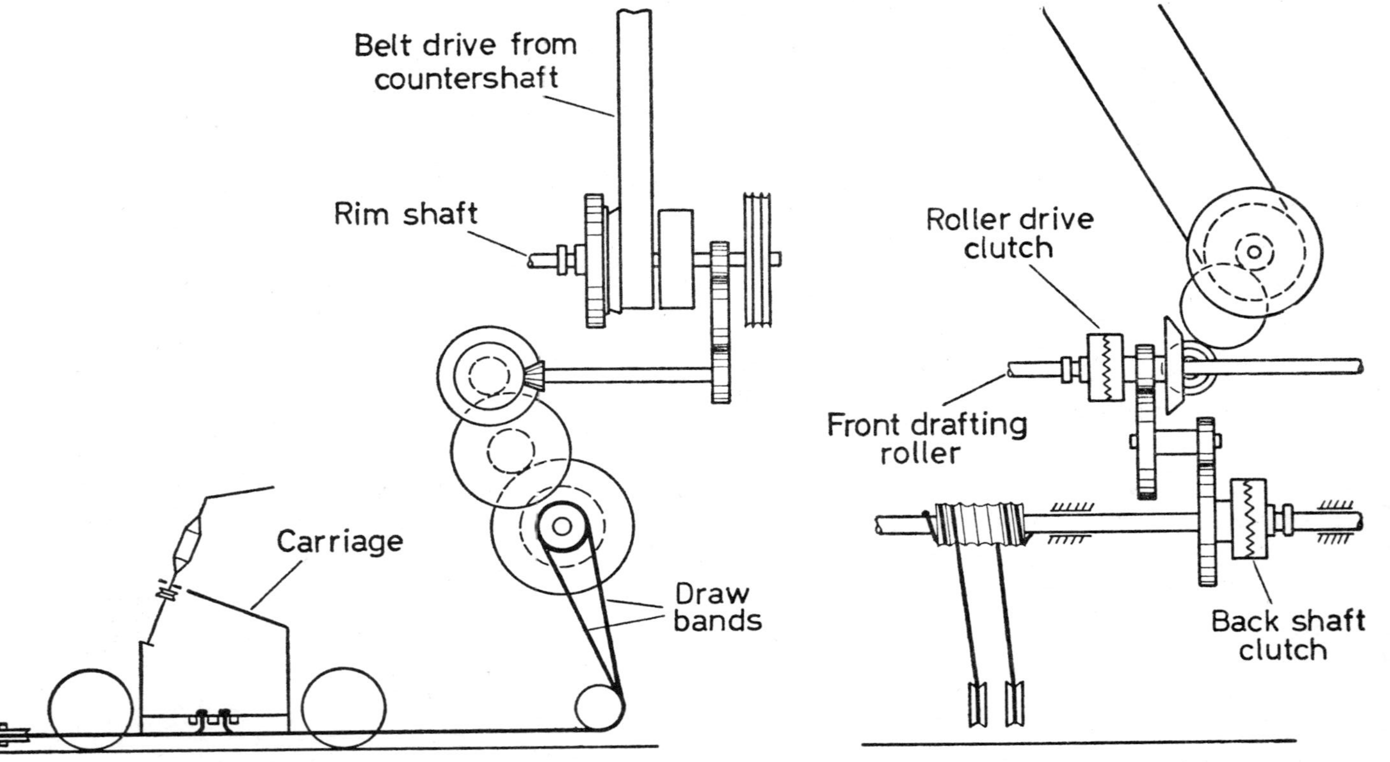

Fig 17. Drive to carriage and rollers during spinning. On a long mule there would be six or eight sets of draw bands spaced along the back shaft, which extended along the whole length of the mule

scroll shaft through bevel gears and a conical friction clutch, the taking-up friction.

Because the quadrant, and hence the spindles, were driven by the inward movement of the carriage, all the energy for accelerating and decelerating both the carriage and the spindles was transmitted through the scroll bands, but the back shaft had still a part to play. Although free from the rim shaft during the run-in it remained coupled to the carriage through both outer and inner draw bands and thus served to distribute the energy along the carriage and maintain the carriage parallel to the roller beam. One might ask why the back shaft itself could not have been fitted with constant acceleration scrolls to avoid the seeming duplication of carriage-driving means. The answer is simple enough. During the draw it was vital that the speed of the carriage should be very precisely related to the speed of delivery of roving from the drafting rollers. This could only be ensured by the use of cylindrical drums on the back shaft.

The mechanisms used to effect the engagement and disengagement of the various drives became highly refined in the later self-actors. Highs, Hargreaves and Crompton had been content to leave control of the initiation and duration of each part of the spinning cycle to the judgment of the operator. It was not long, however, before automatic devices were introduced. The patent for powered working of the mule, obtained by Kelly in 1792, disclosed means for automatically controlling the amount of twist put into the yarn by 'a screw on the axle working into a wheel, the number of teeth in which governs the number of revolutions of the rim by disengaging the rope from the fast to the loose pulley'. Most mules built after this date had some means for automatic engagement and disengagement of the rim-shaft drive.

The most important disengagement needed was that of the carriage drive on completion of the draw. Failure to disengage could result in expensive damage to the machine, but in addition an increasingly vital consideration arose from wage agreements, which were dependent on the length of the draw. On most early mules the drive to the carriage during spinning was through a Mendoza wheel. One of the train of gears from the rim shaft to the back

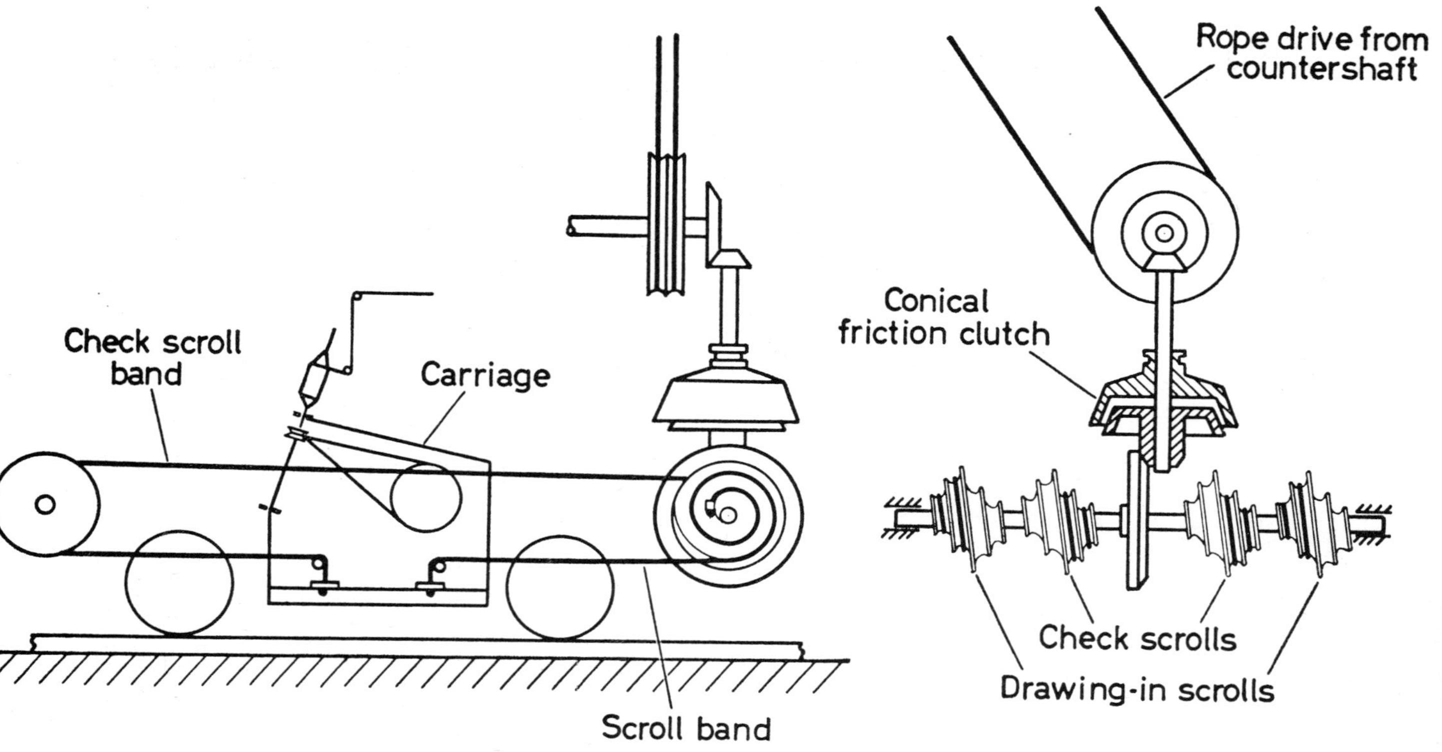

Fig 18. Drive to carriage when winding. Unlike the back shaft, which extended the full length of the mule the scroll shaft was short and directly controlled the carriage only at the headstock

shaft was mounted on an arm pivoted about the axis of the preceding gear in the train. During the draw this gear, the Mendoza wheel, was held in engagement with the succeeding gear in the train by means of a spring or a weight. On completion of the draw the Mendoza wheel was lifted clear of the succeeding gear, thus interrupting the drive. This may seem a rather brutal form of clutch, but in practice it worked well because engagement was made as the belt was being shifted to the fast pulley and was completed before full power was available. Disengagement, of course, presented no problem. It was regarded as a useful feature of the system that the Mendoza wheel would jump out of gear in the event of anyone being trapped by the moving carriage. As speeds increased a form of dog clutch, the axially engaged toothed catch box of the type shown in Fig 17, was introduced. The catch box perhaps never completely displaced the Mendoza wheel but on mules built after about 1875 it was by far the more common device.

The drive to the rollers was always closely related to the drive to the carriage. Although on the simplest mules it would have been possible to use a single catch box or Mendoza wheel common to both the back shaft and the roller drive, in conjunction with an automatic free wheel in the roller drive to permit the carriage to run-in without contra-rotation of the rollers, it was usual to have an additional catch box of the axially engaged type in the roller drive.

Frictional coupling devices were used for engagement of the backing-off and taking-up drives. Various fast and loose pulley systems were used from time to time but conical friction clutches were far more widely adopted. Although fast and loose pulley taking-up remained a feature of mules for very fine counts, the friction became almost universal for backing-off.

The backing-off friction was mounted on the rim shaft itself, the male member usually being made integral with, and slightly larger in diameter than, the fast pulley of the rim shaft. When a taking-up friction was used it was mounted in different positions by different makers, the most common position being on a short vertical shaft at the back of the headstock (Fig 18). Frictions generally worked very well indeed, giving a smooth but rapid take-up of the drive.

The working surface of the female member was of highly polished cast iron and the mating surface of the male member was of specially prepared hard leather, about $\frac{3}{8}$ in thick, riveted to an iron core.

The early mechanisms by which these belts, couplings and clutches were actuated were intrinsically powered, that is, movement of a working element of the mule was used to achieve engagement or disengagement. For such actuating mechanisms to work reliably and consistently they had to be carefully designed and nicely adjusted, or there was a danger that a drive would be partly engaged before an earlier action had been fully disengaged. In the early days particularly, and to a lesser extent throughout the whole period during which mules were built, a great deal of ingenuity was expended in the evolution of reliable, non-critical linkages to engage spur gears and bevel gears (and later catch boxes and frictions) both crisply and accurately. As the size and speed of mules increased a system of powered actuation introduced by Roberts gained in popularity.

The Roberts system of power-shift employed a single cam-shaft carrying a number of cams—one for the control of each drive. The cam-shaft itself was driven intermittently from a constant-speed shaft through a spring-loaded conical friction clutch arranged so that, on engagement, it drove the cam-shaft through exactly half a revolution before automatically disengaging itself. As engagement was achieved by the action of a very light trigger mechanism, great precision of timing was combined with the provision of enough power to move heavy belts and engage or disengage friction clutches. Although the powered cam-shaft led to the use of clumsy 'strong arm' methods of actuation and the disappearance of the elegant, beautifully balanced linkages of earlier days, it was probably justified in the interests of reliability and easy maintenance. Certainly the majority of makers, including Platt Bros, Hetheringtons, Asa Lees and Taylor Lang used cam-shafts widely: but two very successful firms, Threlfalls and Dobson & Barlows, preferred direct actuation by the long-lever system.

The usual form of cam-shaft made one half-revolution at the end of the inward run and simultaneously disengaged the taking-up friction; engaged the back shaft catch box (or lowered the Mendoza wheel); engaged the drafting rollers catch box; moved the guiding fork of the rim shaft driving belt to the fast pulley position against the tension of a spring, and caused it to be retained by a trip latch.

At the end of the outward run the second half-revolution was made: this disengaged the back shaft catch box (or lifted the Mendoza wheel); disengaged the drafting rollers catch box; and re-set a trip mechanism which, on completion of twisting at the head, would release the rim shaft driving belt fork and engage the backing-off friction. At the same time a spring was charged for later engagement of the taking-up friction.

On completion of the second half-revolution of the cam-shaft, the rim shaft driving belt remained on the fast pulley to continue twisting at the head until the revolution-counting gear on the rim shaft (or, sometimes, on the tin roller shaft) caused the trip mechanism to operate and, in rapid succession, move the belt onto the loose pulley and engage the backing-off friction.

Engagement of the backing-off friction acted at first as an extremely effective brake before finally causing the rim shaft and spindles to rotate backwards. The associated backward rotation of the tin roller was used, through a simple freewheel mechanism, to pull the winding faller down to its working position. Thus the movement of the winding faller during backing-off was directly related to the contra-rotation of the spindles and the consequent release of the yarn from the upper part of the spindle blade. As the winding faller reached its operating position it released a trip mechanism which disengaged the backing-off friction clutch, released a catch locating the carriage in the 'at the head' position, coupled the winding drum to the tin roller shaft and engaged the taking-up friction clutch.

Taking up then proceeded until, on completion of the run-in, the arrival of the carriage at its innermost position triggered a further half-revolution of the cam-shaft to restart the cycle of operations.

For some types of yarn the situation was complicated by a need to limit the increasing yarn tension which had resulted from prolonged twisting at the head. Mules intended for the spinning of such yarns were provided with a receding motion. It was probably so called because in jenny and hand mule spinning it had been the practice to allow the clove of the jenny, or the carriage of the hand mule, to recede a little during the insertion of supplementary twist. On self-actors it was found to be more convenient to achieve the same end by causing the rollers to rotate slowly and deliver a short length of additional roving during twisting at the head. A further complication, sometimes added, was a mechanism to halt the rollers a few inches before the end of the draw to achieve jacking of the yarn. This was the pulling out of the thicker, softer-twisted portions of the yarn in order to obtain greater uniformity of thickness.

A particularly interesting device used in later mules was one which gave a supplementary delivery of roving from the rollers during the run-in of the carriage. This was popularly regarded as a somewhat reprehensible expedient for increasing the effective length of the mule draw at the expense of yarn quality. In fact it served rather to improve yarn quality by giving a better distribution of twist in the final yarn. During winding the yarn had to pass over two faller wires under considerable tension, and this tended to hold back the twist and caused the yarn wound in the later part of the run-in to contain more twist than that wound in the early part. (This effect can easily be appreciated by taking a length of tape, twisting it, and while holding the two ends, run it over the sharp edge of a desk or table. It will be found that the sharp edge acts as a twist barrier and holds back the twist.) By progressively diluting the twist with the addition of untwisted roving as winding-on proceeded, supplementary roller delivery motions offset the twist-barrier effect of the two faller wires and gave a more uniform distribution of twist in the yarn wound onto the cop.

Some hand mules had been fitted with cams to control the guiding of the yarn during winding but it had been usual to leave this to the skill of the spinners. In his patent of 1792. William Kelly had spoken of shaping the cop by means of an inclined plane and this system of winding control was refined and used in the self-actor. In its commonest form the system used two inclined planes which remained stationary while being traversed by a bowl and lever attached to the moving carriage. A typical arrangement is shown in Fig 19. The bowl and lever followed the profile of the copping rail both when spinning and when winding: but during spinning the faller itself was held clear above the yarn sheet by a spring acting on a control arm secured to the faller shaft.

It has already been explained that contra-rotation of the tin roller during backing-off brought the winding faller into its working position. The action can be more completely understood by reference to Fig 19. Reverse rotation of the tin roller caused a pawl to engage and rotate a ratchet wheel mounted freely on the tin-roller shaft. A drum attached to the ratchet wheel wound up a chain connected to a sector on the faller shaft and rotated the faller shaft against the pull of a spring. As the faller was depressed the boot leg, a strut pendant from the control arm, was raised until, as the faller reached its working position, the lower end of the boot leg latched onto a stud fixed to the end of the copping lever. (In Fig 19 the boot leg can be seen in the latched position, the carriage having completed about one-third of the inward run. The trigger mechanism by which backing-off was terminated and winding was initiated by the latching action is not shown.) During the run-in the lever followed the profile of the copping rail and determined the path of the faller until, at the end of the inward run, the boot leg was unlatched from the copping lever stud on striking the unlocking bracket, a fixed member carried by the headstock frame.

The faller and the counterfaller were so linked that depression of the faller during backing-off freed the counterfaller and allowed it to apply tension to the yarn sheet. The return of the faller to the spinning position was accompanied by automatic interlocking of the linkage to maintain both wires in the spinning position.

The shape of the copping rail was such as to give the quick-down/slow-up traverse of the cop chase needed to form the traditional cop. The whole rail was gradually lowered during the building up of the cop so as to cause the chase to rise progressively up the spindle. The gradual lowering was achieved by the withdrawal of ramps, known as builder cams, from beneath the rail. This was done to a linear programme by a simple screw and gear-nut mech-

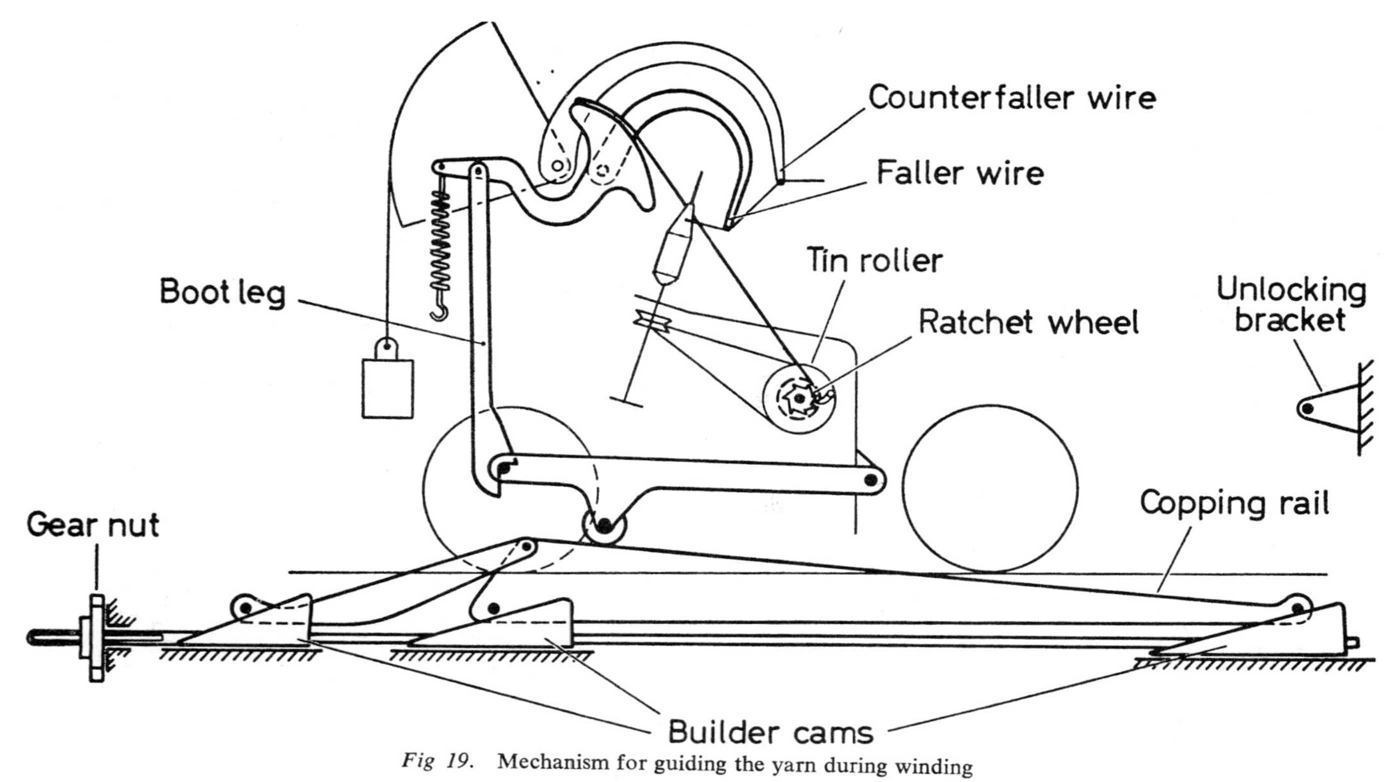

Fig 19. Mechanism for guiding the yarn during winding

anism. To form the ideal cop shape it was necessary to vary the length of the chase quite appreciably during cop formation. Initially the chase of a typical cop was about 1·2 in long. During formation of the cop bottom the chase length was almost doubled to about 2·3 in and thereafter it was progressively reduced to about 1·4 in on completion of the cop.

This rather complex construction had been evolved by hand spinners in their efforts to produce the ideal shuttle package—a package of great mechanical strength yet containing the maximum length of yarn consistent with satisfactory unwinding in the shuttle. Early self-actors had a one-piece copping rail and were unable to achieve this refinement in cop shaping. From about 1875 onwards the copping rail was made in two parts, hinged at the apex. Three linked builder cams were provided to give the necessary vertical location to the two ends of the rail and the hinged apex respectively. Horizontal location was by means of a single, near-vertical slot in which a peg, fixed to the main body of the rail, was free to slide. With this arrangement the most subtle variations of cop chase proportions were possible and a great deal of care and patience was lavished on the shaping of sets of builder cams to meet particular needs.

Although the arrangement of copping rail just described was by far the most widely used, an alternative, known as the short rail, was often used on fine mules. Basically the arrangement was the same. Each of the elements of the mechanism had its exact counterpart with identical functions. The great difference was that the rail, instead of being the same length as the draw and fixed to the floor, was only about 16 in long, was carried on slides fixed to the carriage and was moved relative to the carriage (and hence relative to the copping-lever bowl) by differential gearing. The claim of the short rail was that, by changing the ratio of the gearing, the mule could be set to work with a shorter draw for the spinning of exceptionally fine yarns. The value of this claim is rather dubious as too many other factors, particularly those concerned with the operation of the quadrant, would be upset by a change of draw length for it to seem likely that it was frequently done.

The above description of the self-actor, complex as it is, does no more than outline the common form of the machine. Innumerable variations to meet real or fancied shortcomings of the usual mechanism appeared from time to time. Many of these were irrelevancies of no positive value but in addition there were a number which became established for special purposes, notably for the spinning of very fine yarns and very coarse yarns. The more important of them are discussed in the next chapter.

6

Growth to Maturity

ROBERTS was a restless, versatile genius. He did not spend the rest of his life perfecting the self-actor but soon moved on to solve other interesting problems in diverse fields of engineering. Although the machine he had evolved embodied all the elements needed for complete self-action, he did not linger on the scene to guide and encourage spinners and other machinery makers in the fullest use of the more advanced features of his complex design. Two of these features, the nosing motion and the strapping motion, are of sufficient interest and importance to warrant consideration in some detail.

For reasons concerned with the suitability of the cop as a yarn package for the weaver's shuttle, it was desirable that the mule spindle should be markedly tapered, typically from about $\frac{5}{16}$ in diameter immediately above the spindle rail to about $\frac{1}{10}$ in diameter at the tip. This requirement led to a difficulty in winding which may not be readily apparent to the reader. The basis of the difficulty lies in the fact that, if snarling at let-in is to be avoided, the rate at which yarn is being wound onto the cop during the last few inches of the inward run of the carriage must be not less than the rate of inward movement of the carriage itself. During this critical period of the inward run, winding took place on the nose of the cop. Here the winding diameter was least, closely approaching the diameter of the spindle blade. To take account of this it was necessary for the spindle speed to increase rapidly as the carriage approached the end of the inward run. The basic quadrant mechanism was able to cope with the situation throughout the early and middle stages of cop formation: but in the final stages, when the full effect of spindle-blade taper demanded high accelerations, it was not quite able to do the task. To enable the additional acceleration to be achieved, Roberts provided a supplementary device which could be brought into action by the spinner as cop formation proceeded.

The action of the device, known as a nosing motion, is illustrated in Fig 20. It consisted of a substantial peg carried by a slotted member integral with the quadrant arm. Immediately after doffing, the peg was secured at the extreme inboard end of the slot, in which position it was inoperative. As cop formation proceeded and nosing action became necessary, the nosing peg was moved out along the slot so that during the last few inches of the inward run of the carriage it came into contact with, and deflected, the winding chain and thus accelerated the spindles.

An analysis of the performance of the quadrant winding mechanism has shown that without a supplementary nosing motion it was unable to provide satisfactory winding conditions during the last quarter of the total period of formation of a cop. During this period increasing difficulty would be experienced as progressive reduction in the diameter of the cop nose caused the rate of winding, during the last few inches of carriage movement, to fall further below the corresponding rate of yarn release. The difficulty would be manifest by a small but increasing excess of yarn on completion of laying-on. At first the snarl formed by this excess would be small enough to be pulled out by the carriage draft during the early part of the draw. Although undesirable this situation would be tolerable. As cop formation proceeded the excess of yarn would increase until a time came when the snarl could no longer be pulled out and it would be necessary to apply some remedial action. As many mules were built and operated without nosing motions it is interesting to speculate as to what remedial action was taken.

For coarse, low-twist yarns, suitable for use as weft in blankets and raised sheets, conditions were probably just tolerable. On mules used to make these yarns the spindles were only slightly tapered

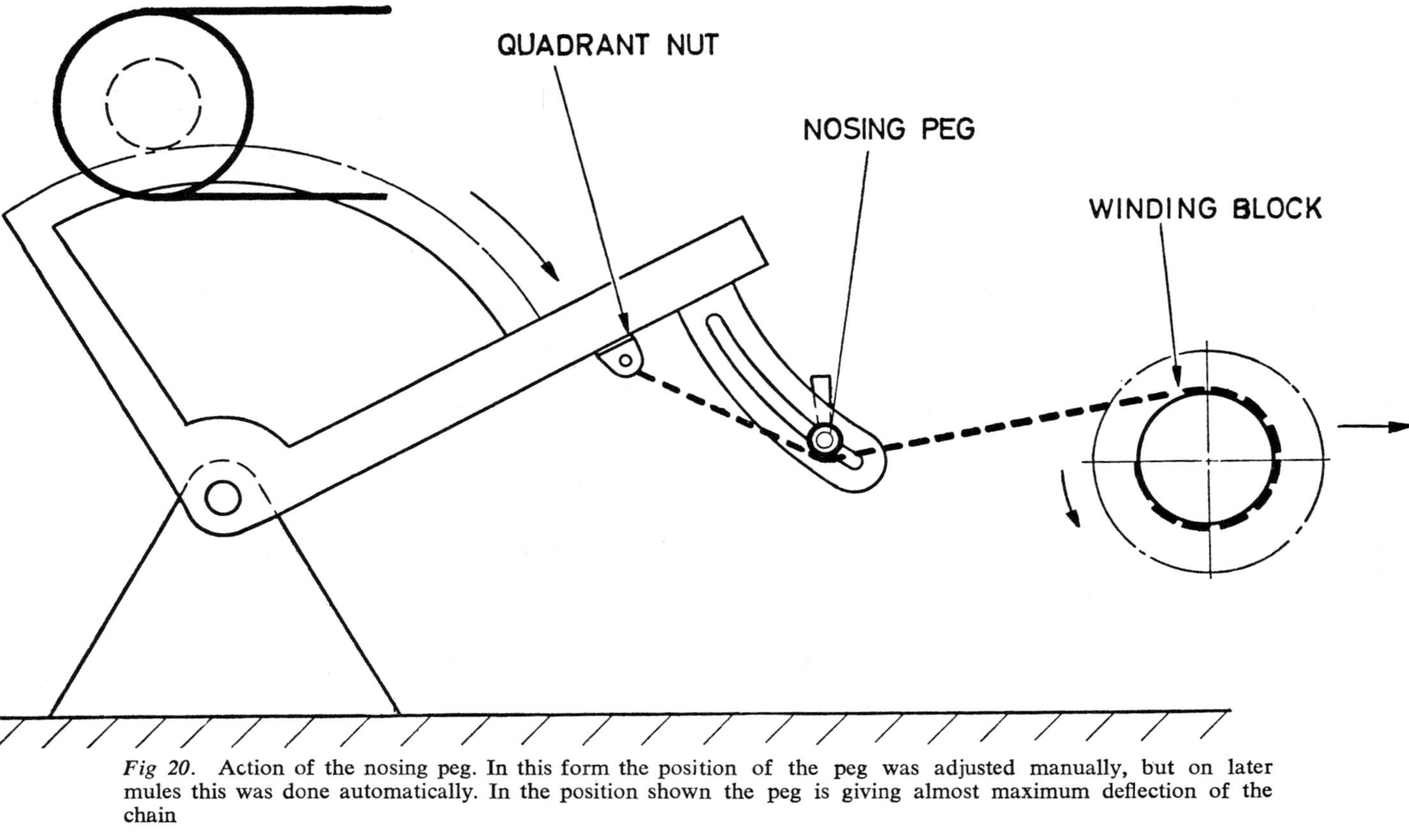

Fig 20. Action of the nosing peg. In this form the position of the peg was adjusted manually, but on later mules this was done automatically. In the position shown the peg is giving almost maximum deflection of the chain

and the complication of a nosing motion was rejected for many years. Under more typical conditions it was essential to do something to prevent excessive snarling in the late stages of cop formation. Perhaps the simplest palliative action was that of manually delaying the rise of the winding faller during the last few inches of winding, and permitting it to rise to the spinning position only when the outward movement of the carriage had begun. Because the first outward movement of the carriage was accompanied by extremely rapid acceleration of the spindles to spinning speed, this operation demanded a certain measure of skill and dexterity. It was, however, a practicable method of preventing the formation of snarls when an excess of yarn remained on completion of the inward run. On later mules, equipped with effective nosing motions, this technique was used by spinners when engaged in the setting-up of the winding mechanism by trial-and-error methods.

Although simple enough, this palliative had the drawback that an operative had to be in close attendance on the mule for each run-in during the later stages of formation of each set of cops. This may seem a serious objection today, but it must be remembered that in the early years of the self-actor, hand-mule spinners were required to control (and provide the driving power for) every inward run of the mule throughout the whole cycle of cop formation. A mule which was completely self-acting for most of the time and required only a little manual assistance during the critical last hour or so before doffing must have seemed a veritable paragon.

Despite this it was not long before a mechanical arrangement known as the hastening motion was introduced. It cannot be regarded as a true nosing motion, but rather as a time-saving device: it did achieve a substantial measure of nosing action without demanding either manual dexterity or constant attendance. Normally during winding the rim shaft was free and the spindles were driven only by the quadrant winding mechanism. On completion of the inward run the rim shaft belt was moved onto the fast pulley and the spindles accelerated to spinning speed. The hastening motion was a device by which an adjustable cam, mounted on the carriage, could be set to move the rim-shaft driving belt onto the fast pulley a little before termination of the inward run. Thornley describes the action in this way:

> When the strap is thus put upon the fast pulley the spindles are immediately accelerated in speed by receiving their motion from the rim shaft, instead of the winding drum, two inches or so before the end of the inwards run. By this means the hastening motion becomes an important factor in preventing snarls and in winding better cop noses.

In the early forms of the device, the setting of the cam could be varied manually by means of a thumbscrew. The mechanism was allowed to remain in an inoperative condition until the later stages of cop formation were reached. The cam would then be gradually raised to give progressively earlier acceleration of the spindles as formation of the cops approached completion. Means were later contrived by which the cam was raised automatically, but there is reason to believe that the hastening motion alone was never regarded as a completely satisfactory solution to the problem of nosing. The most likely explanation for this is that the accuracy of control needed to wind on less than 1 in of yarn with some precision could not be achieved reliably by the partial engagement of a powerful driving belt capable of accelerating the spindles from rest to 8,000 rpm in less than three seconds. This view is supported by the fact that Thornley offers advice to practical spinners on the avoidance of sawneys resulting from unduly keen action of the hastening motion.

In contrast to this temperamental and distinctly brutal device, the nosing peg was an instrument of great precision. It is surprising, therefore, that the hastening motion was devised and used at all at a time when the nosing peg was already available. A possible explanation lies in the fact that Roberts did not maintain close contact with the spinners and other textile-machinery makers. By and large they were men of a type preferring ad hoc devices, involving the critical adjustment of belts and frictions, to the kinematic precision of such devices as delighted Roberts. This is consistent with the general character of all the pre-Roberts attempts at the design of a self-actor. If the nosing peg, exactly as provided by Roberts, did not function satisfactorily, then—not understanding it and having no sympathy with the kinematic approach—they would almost certainly reject it and attempt such a solution as that offered by the hastening motion.

Whatever the explanation, the hastening motion continued long in widespread use while numerous individual inventors proceeded to devise variants on the Roberts' nosing peg. Many of these were quite satisfactory, and by about 1870 every machinery maker offered self-acting mules on the Roberts principle fitted with nosing motions dependent for their action on deflection of the winding chain by an adjustable peg. In some cases the adjustment was automatic and programmed but others relied upon manual adjustment by the spinner. For most purposes these devices were completely satisfactory.

One machinery maker, however, regarded the nosing peg as falling short of perfection and developed the only alternative arrangement which was to become at all widely used. The arrangement, which was fitted to most mules built by Platt Bros after 1875, was described by Eli Spencer in the *Proceedings of the Institution of Mechanical Engineers* in 1880. It was known as the scroll-drum nosing motion and is shown schematically in Fig 21.

Instead of the usual plain cylindrical winding block, a combined cylinder and scroll of reducing radius was used. The proportions were such that, during the early stages of cop formation, only the cylindrical portion of the winding block was used and the action of the quadrant winding mechanism was perfectly normal. As nosing action became necessary it was arranged that the end of the winding chain normally secured to the quadrant nut was progressively wound onto a small winch embodied in a special quadrant nut. The effect of this was to bring into use the scroll portion of the winding block and thereby accelerate the rotation of the spindles during the last few inches of the inward movement of the carriage. As cop formation proceeded, more chain was taken up by the winch and the scroll portion of the winding block was brought into use even earlier. Thus the amount of nosing was progressively increased.

This was a particularly elegant mechanism of which even Roberts himself might well have been proud. The flexibility of the design,

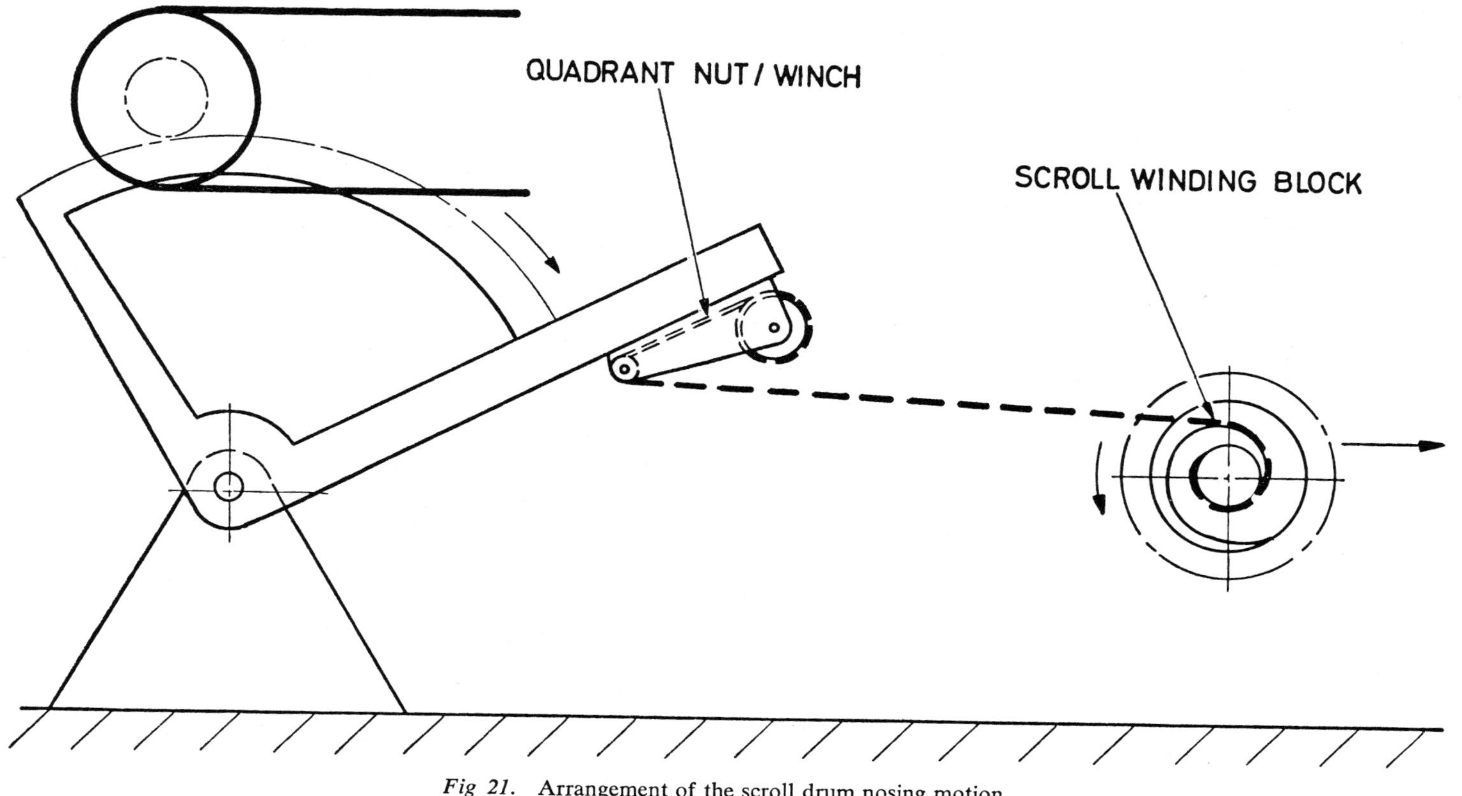

Fig 21. Arrangement of the scroll drum nosing motion

inherent in the scroll-drum principle, permitted an almost unlimited degree of nosing action to be achieved with the greatest precision. Its potential was certainly very much greater than that of the more circumscribed nosing-peg mechanism, though it did not completely displace the earlier device: most makers continued to develop even more elaborate versions of the nosing peg, and only Platt Bros made a motion of the scroll-drum type. However, as almost half of all the mules set up in Britain after 1870 were made up by Platts, the scroll-drum type was obviously extremely successful; whether the high reputation of the Platts' mule was because of, or in spite of, its unique nosing motion was a point that was often debated. Certainly Spencer regarded the scroll-drum motion as being unquestionably superior to even the most highly developed form of the nosing peg; this he condemns by saying that it '. . . commences too early, is limited in its action and appears to lose its accelerating function when it ought to be greatest'.

Scott-Taggart, writing in 1899, also regarded the nosing peg as inadequate but for reasons diametrically opposed to those advanced by Spencer. Scott-Taggart complained that 'It (the nosing peg) has some very serious faults . . . in the first place the action starts too late. . . .' Clearly the nosing peg had some limitations but they could not have been serious as nosing motions on this principle were made right up to the end and, despite the popularity of their scroll drum motion, some of the Platt Bros customers insisted on having the older mechanism fitted to new mules.

Like the nosing motion the strapping motion too was, for many years, rejected by practical spinners. Both the concept and the principles of operation were far too advanced to be accepted by the technologists of the early nineteenth century and Roberts did not live to see the validation of what has proved to be perhaps the most important contribution of the century to the theory and practice of automatic control. In the provision of an error-actuated servo-mechanism for the control of a discontinuous process, Roberts was a true innovator. Although the strapping motion was not widely used during the next fifty years, this was no reflection on the soundness of the device: it was largely because it offered a degree of automation beyond the requirements of the age. When, many years later, it gained almost universal acceptance it was in a form little different from that described in Roberts' patent specification of 1830.

The function of the strapping motion was the progressive movement of the quadrant nut along the quadrant arm, which was needed to take account of the increasing diameter of the cop chase during formation of the cop bottom. The motion was so called because in its earliest form a flat leather belt or strap was the most conspicuous component of the mechanism. The most interesting feature of its action was that during each inward run the length of excess yarn formed during winding was automatically, and continuously, referred to a programmed desired length and proportional adjustment was made to the position of the quadrant nut to reduce any discrepancy existing between actual and desired excess length. The need for resetting of the quadrant nut during the formation of the cop bottom is implicit in the concept of the quadrant winding mechanism: but it is by no means obvious that the refinement of error-actuated automatic control was a real need. At the time when the self-actor was being developed, the general problem of winding textile materials onto packages of continuously increasing diameter was an ever-recurring one to which there were already a number of acceptable solutions.

For parallel packages the simple solution of a constant-speed driving drum in frictional contact with the winding surface was widely used, but it was, of course, inapplicable to winding onto a conical surface such as a cop chase. On the roving frame, used to prepare rovings for both water-frame and mule spinning, the problem was satisfactorily solved without recourse to driving on the package surface. Here winding is effected by the relative motion of spindle and flyer, as in the Saxony wheel, water frame and throstle. However, whereas a friction-drag arrangement was satisfactory for the tensioning of spun yarns, a more precise control was needed to avoid damage to the relatively delicate rovings. Roving issues from the delivery rollers of a roving frame at a constant rate, and it is necessary to reduce the speed differential between spindle and flyer progressively as the package diameter increases. The speed differential was varied then, as now, by means of a variable-ratio drive continuously reset, to a programme, as formation of the bobbin proceeded.

Programmed resetting of this sort is open to the fundamental objection that, although the programme may be arranged to deal precisely with roving of a particular nominal thickness, the actual mean thickness of individual rovings is known to vary as much as 4 per cent from the nominal value. Despite this the system is completely successful on roving frames. The explanation is that when the roving is appreciably thicker than that for which the winding speed is programmed, the package diameter naturally tends to increase more rapidly than is catered for by the programme. If the roving were inextensible this would be an impossible state of affairs but, in practice, roving is elastically extensible and winding is able to continue with the roving subject to a somewhat greater tension. The increased winding tension leads to more effective compacting of the layers of roving, thereby limiting the undue increase in package diameter which would otherwise occur. Thus the net result of small deviations in the mean thickness of the roving is merely a small increase in winding tension. Winding conditions on the mule were, however, very much more critical.

For a given mule the length of yarn spun during each draw, and hence the length to be wound onto the cop during the run-in, was absolutely constant. The necessary length of free yarn on completion of winding depended on the stage of development of the cop. On a typical mule the length to be wound was about 63 in and the desired excess length on completion of the run-in was progressively reduced from a maximum of about 12 in in the early stages of cop formation to about 6 in as cop formation neared completion. Consider what would have happened on a mule with correctly programmed resetting of the quadrant nut when, for one reason or another, the mean diameter of the yarn was 4 per cent greater than the nominal diameter. As the counterfaller mechanism ensured a substantially constant winding tension the diameter of the cop would inevitably have increased more rapidly than was catered for by the quadrant resetting programme. Suppose the mean cop diameter to have reached a value 2 per cent greater than that assumed in the programme. The mule would then have proceeded to wind onto the cop chase a length of yarn 2 per cent (roughly $1\frac{1}{4}$ in) greater than the length spun in the immediately preceding draw. During actual winding the counterfaller would automatically accommodate the excessive winding rate and the moment of reckoning would be delayed until, at the end of the run-in, the deficiency of $1\frac{1}{4}$ in in the length of yarn available for laying-on would be dramatically revealed by a sawney, the simultaneous breakage of all the threads.

For the successful operation of a system of programmed winding control it would have been necessary to control the mean yarn diameter to an accuracy of 0·5 per cent. Even today, with the most refined count-control techniques, this cannot be done. It was necessary therefore to employ some form of data feedback, some system of error actuated control. By far the simplest means was manual resetting of the quadrant nut by an operative in close attendance on the mule and this was the means employed for many years. The strapping motion was devised to do the same thing automatically.

The earliest form of the motion, described in Roberts' 1830 patent, is illustrated in Fig 22. The error-detecting element was the counterfaller itself. The proportions and disposition of an arm secured to the counterfaller shaft, the slotted link, 1, and the weighted lever, 2, relative to the anvil, 3, were such that, when the length of excess yarn during winding became less than the desired value, the strap was gripped between a projection on the weighted lever and the anvil. When this occurred the motion of the carriage was transmitted through the lever and anvil to the strap. Movement of the strap, through bevel gears at the quadrant fulcrum, turned the quadrant screw in the direction to cause the quadrant nut to move radially outwards. Increasing the quadrant radius immediately reduced the speed at which the spindles were being driven and hence reduced the rate at which yarn was being wound up. Movement of the strap, and corresponding reduction in the spindle speed, continued until the excess length of yarn was restored to the desired value, the counterfaller rose to its correct height, and the lever and anvil released their grip on the strap.

Just how successful the original form of the strapping motion

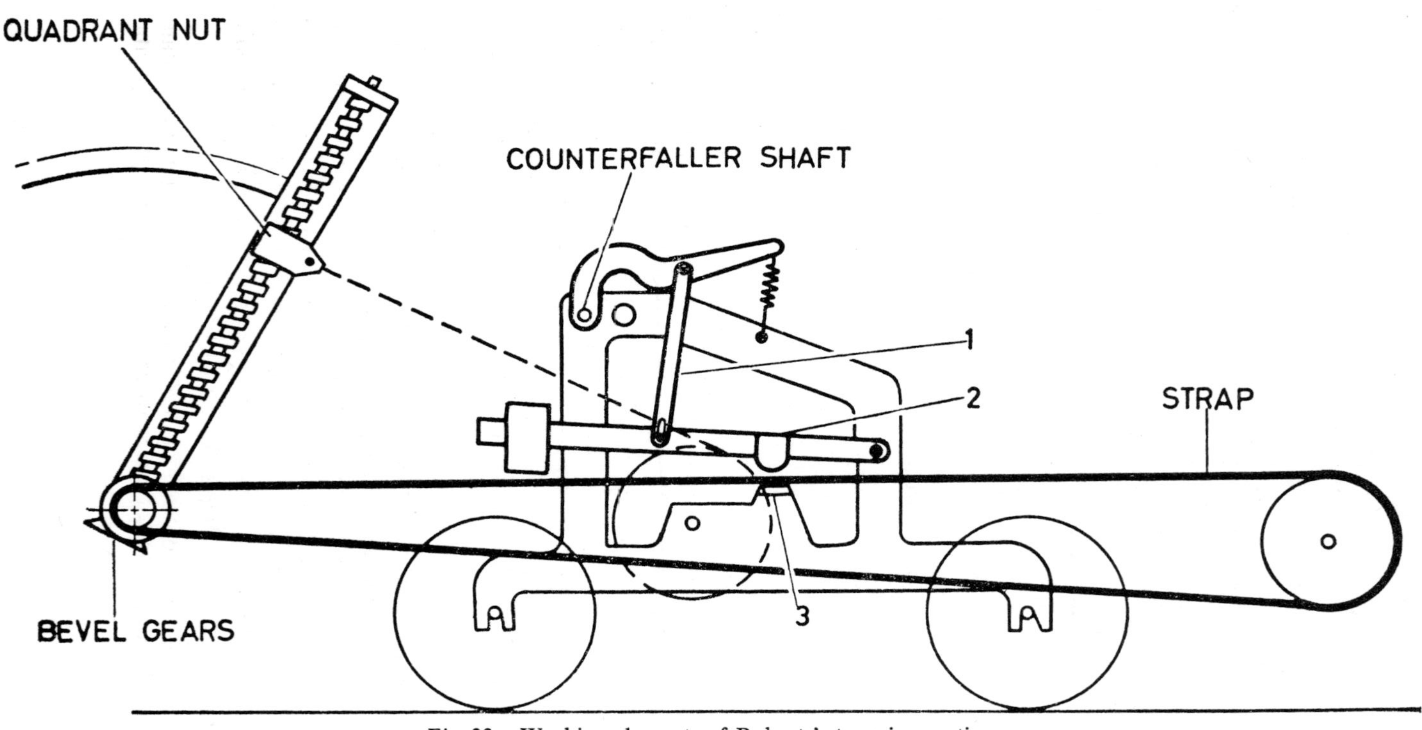

Fig 22. Working elements of Roberts' strapping motion

was is hard to say. Although some mules were made without any form of automatic resetting of the quadrant nut, many were fitted with minor variants on the Roberts arrangement. The amount of work involved in manually resetting the quadrant of an early self-actor not fitted with a strapping motion was indicated in Chapter 5. On a typical mule without a strapping motion roughly ninety manual adjustments of the quadrant-nut position were needed between commencement of a set and the completion of cop-bottom formation, in those days a period of about four hours. An analysis of the performance of the original form of the strapping motion has shown that, although it was not perfect, the spinner needed to make only five small adjustments during cop-bottom formation in order to achieve control of the winding at least as precise as the best direct manual control could give.

This was a considerable advance but it was by no means universally adopted. One reason for this may have been that the need for adjustment arose because the strapping motion tended progressively to over-correct for the increasing cop diameter as cop formation proceeded. Without it a spinner had to be diligent in his resetting of the quadrant-nut position if he was not to suffer the disaster of a sawney. Negligence in the progressive adjustment of a strapping motion merely led to the formation of snarls in the yarn. There can be no doubt that a spinner, paid on a piece rate, would infinitely prefer the risk of snarls, which only inconvenienced the weaver, to even a remote chance of a sawney which would involve him in a great deal of extra work and a loss of pay. Management, however, had other interests. They were, naturally, concerned to maintain the quality of their yarn and the approbation of their customers, and hence reluctant to buy a labour-saving device which increased the risk of faulty yarn.

Kurt Neste in his book *The Mule Spinning Process*, published in 1865, offers evidence that nearly forty years after the invention of the self-actor (by which time there were some 44,000,000 spindles in use in Britain alone) the strapping motion was not universally, and probably not even widely, used. Neste wrote:

> The screw for moving the quadrant nut is turned by hand; various apparatus have been employed to make this regulation

> self-acting, but according to inquiries made of a great number of workmen in different mills, the workman always has still to correct this regulation; so that until now nothing else has been achieved by the self regulating motions, but that the workman has to turn the screw a few times less.

This view was not held by John Platt of Platt Bros or by Peter McGregor of P. & J. McGregor. The former, in a paper published in the *Proceedings of the Institution of Mechanical Engineers* for 1866, after describing in detail the original form of the Roberts strapping motion, concludes: '. . . by this means the threads are wound uniformly upon the cops, with an equal degree of tightness throughout'. A letter written by McGregor in 1872, and quoted by Evan Leigh in his *Science of Modern Cotton Spinning*, says:

> Roberts' plan for regulating the winding on at the beginning of a set of cops, on the bare spindle till the cone is formed, has not been materially improved since his day, as his strapping motion, as it is called in the trade (but with a band instead of a strap), is the simplest plan and just as efficient as any yet made for that purpose, and when properly set is completely self-acting.

This divergence of view is probably accounted for by the fact that Neste was a master spinner writing for the guidance of master spinners, whereas both Platt and McGregor were manufacturers of spinning mules anxious to sell their wares. That the real situation was less perfect than that described by Platt and McGregor is indicated in a paper presented to the Institution of Mechanical Engineers in 1880 by Eli Spencer. Platt was by this time dead but Spencer had been a colleague of his and was still closely associated with the firm of Platt Bros.

> In its general arrangement the Self-Acting Mule remains as described in 1866, but many important additions and improvements have been introduced. The Self-acting mule of 1866, although effecting the principal operations, left a number of minor ones to the skill of the operative spinner or 'minder', and it performed some of its duties in a very imperfect manner.
>
> The first improvement to be noticed is that the governer motion for regulating the position of the quadrant nut has been made at once exceedingly sensitive and very reliable, and is now suitable for either coarse or fine counts.

Spencer's 'exceedingly sensitive and very reliable governor motion' was no more than a logical refinement of Roberts' strapping motion.

Kinematic analysis has shown that the only limitation of the original design was that the motion took no account of the decreasing length of yarn needed for laying-on as cop formation proceeded, but continued to assess the need for quadrant-nut adjustment by comparing the actual excess of yarn during winding to a fixed 'desired excess length'. An intelligent spinner would quickly appre-

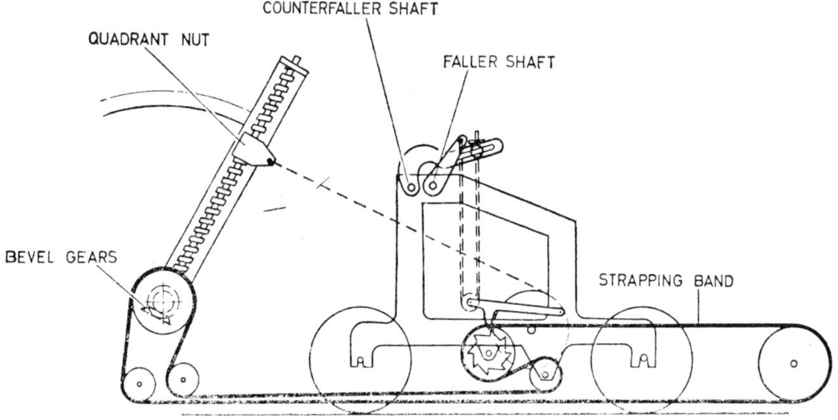

Fig 23. The form of strapping motion used on later mules

ciate this and see that to achieve perfection, all that was needed was a programmed correction of the 'desired excess length'. As the correction needed was simply related to the position of the cop chase on the spindle, it was a perfectly logical step to use the changing position of the winding faller to provide the correction automatically. Fig 23 demonstrates how the motions of the winding faller and the counterfaller were combined to remove the fault.

This arrangement was extremely successful and quickly became established as the usual form of strapping motion. It differed from the original Roberts arrangement in only two respects. The most important of these was the refinement, already mentioned, by which account was taken of the position of the winding faller; and analysis shows that with this refinement the principle of error determination approached perfection. The other difference was of a practical nature and lay in the means by which the strap was caused to move with the carriage when the detection of error called for adjustment of the quadrant nut position. In the original form of the motion the strap was actually a flat leather belt, gripped directly between the error-detecting lever and a fixed anvil. In the new arrangement a cord or band replaced the strap, and V-grooved pulleys replaced the flat pulleys originally used. In addition the band passed round two freely mounted pulleys on the mule carriage. During the inward run of the carriage these pulleys would normally rotate freely, the band remaining stationary. When the length of excess yarn became less than the desired length and correction became necessary, a projection on the error-detecting lever came into contact with the teeth of a ratchet wheel compounded with one of the free pulleys. This stopped the rotation of the pulley relative to the carriage and caused the band to move with the carriage and thus rotate the quadrant screw in the same way as did the old strap. Working in this way, wear on the strap was greatly reduced. The substitution of a rope in V-grooved pulleys for the strap and flat-faced pulleys of the original motion increased the reliability of the friction drive. The net result was a more precise and substantially trouble-free mechanism which still operated on the principle established by Roberts fifty years earlier.

Not only was this later form of strapping motion kinematically correct, it was also extremely successful in day-to-day use. This is not to say that it always worked perfectly. Then, as now, practical men, without formal understanding of the principles of operation of a sophisticated device, would prefer to meet shortcomings by direct corrective action rather than attempt the more difficult task of adjusting a slightly imperfect automatic controller. It is probable, therefore, that not all motions were set to best advantage at a time when it was the practice, throughout all branches of the industry, to treat each machine as an individual having its own idiosyncrasies. Yet the improved strapping motion worked extremely well and quickly gained very wide acceptance, being fitted not only to new machines but also as a conversion to older ones.

From the literature, and from discussions with old mule spinners, it appears that few, if any, strapping motions were so good that the winding conditions could not be improved by a little personal attention from the minder. Thornley, however, writing in 1885, was of the opinion that all strapping motions then made were able to give satisfactory control when in proper order and that the best gave even better control than could be achieved by the most careful spinner. In the event the strapping motion was never superseded. Machinery makers continued to bring out novel regulators to remedy this or that alleged deficiency of the established system. Some of these regulators were highly complex, others showed remarkable ingenuity: but none combined the basic soundness and robust simplicity of Roberts' masterpiece, and none succeeded in displacing the strapping motion.

7

Bolton Style

DURING the eighteenth century the fine muslins imported from India, although almost unbelievably expensive, were very highly prized and continued to grow in popularity. The high labour costs involved in spinning the yarn for such fabrics made it hopelessly uneconomic to attempt their manufacture in Europe until the invention of the mule made machine-spinning of muslin yarns possible. There followed a quite remarkable increase in the demand for fine cotton fabrics and the Bolton area, in which the mule had been invented and first used, quickly established a reputation for the spinning of very fine yarns of the highest quality.

This reputation continued to grow. At the time of the introduction of mule spinning 80's was reckoned a very fine yarn: but fifty years later 350's[1] was a standard article of commerce sold in substantial quantities. During the same period a quite dramatic reduction occurred in the cost of fine yarns. In the early 1780s the cost of 1 lb of 100's cotton was about £2: but by 1830 it had fallen to only 3s (15 p). The reduction was almost entirely the result of the developments in the application of power to the mule.

The introduction of the self-actor did not at first affect the spinning of fine yarns. The early machines were neither so precise nor so gentle in their action as was necessary, and their use was

[1] (350's cotton is of the same order of fineness, but has only about one-quarter of the strength, of 15 denier nylon such as is used for fine sheer stockings.)

largely confined to the spinning of the coarser yarns. A great deal of attention was paid to refinement of the self-actor but progress in application to fine spinning was slow. In the very early days James Montgomery, in the 1836 edition of his practical treatise, *Theory and Practice of Cotton Spinning*, recommended the self-actor for counts up to 50's and the mule jenny for counts from 40's upwards. The progress made during the next thirty years can be judged from the statement by Neste in 1865:

> Self-acting mules are applicable from the coarsest numbers up to 110, but they are seldom found in use for finer numbers than 80. The finer yarns are spun on hand mules.

By 1880 Eli Spencer of Platt Bros was able to write:

> For spinning yarns of medium fine counts, say up to No 90, the self-acting mule has now almost entirely superseded the hand mule. The work is excellent, both in quality and quantity.

By this time self-actors were becoming suitable for finer yarns and a considerable degree of local concentration and specialisation of the industry had taken place. At the beginning of the nineteenth century both spinning and weaving were carried on in almost all the small towns of South Lancashire and in some towns in Cheshire, Derbyshire and Scotland. The most striking feature of the pattern which emerged was the specialisation of the more northerly towns of Lancashire on weaving and of the southerly towns on spinning and finishing. Within this pattern there was a clearly defined sub-pattern. Oldham grew to be the predominant spinning town for coarse yarns while Bolton came to specialise in the spinning of fine yarns.

As the industry approached its zenith these two geographically dissimilar towns, Oldham on a hill and Bolton in a valley, came to dominate the spinning scene. By 1905, out of a total of roughly 50,000,000 spindles, more than half were in the two towns. Oldham had 17,000,000 spindles working mainly in the count range 20's to 60's while Bolton had 10,000,000 spindles largely used for the finer counts. The distribution of the Lancashire industry was as shown in Fig 24.

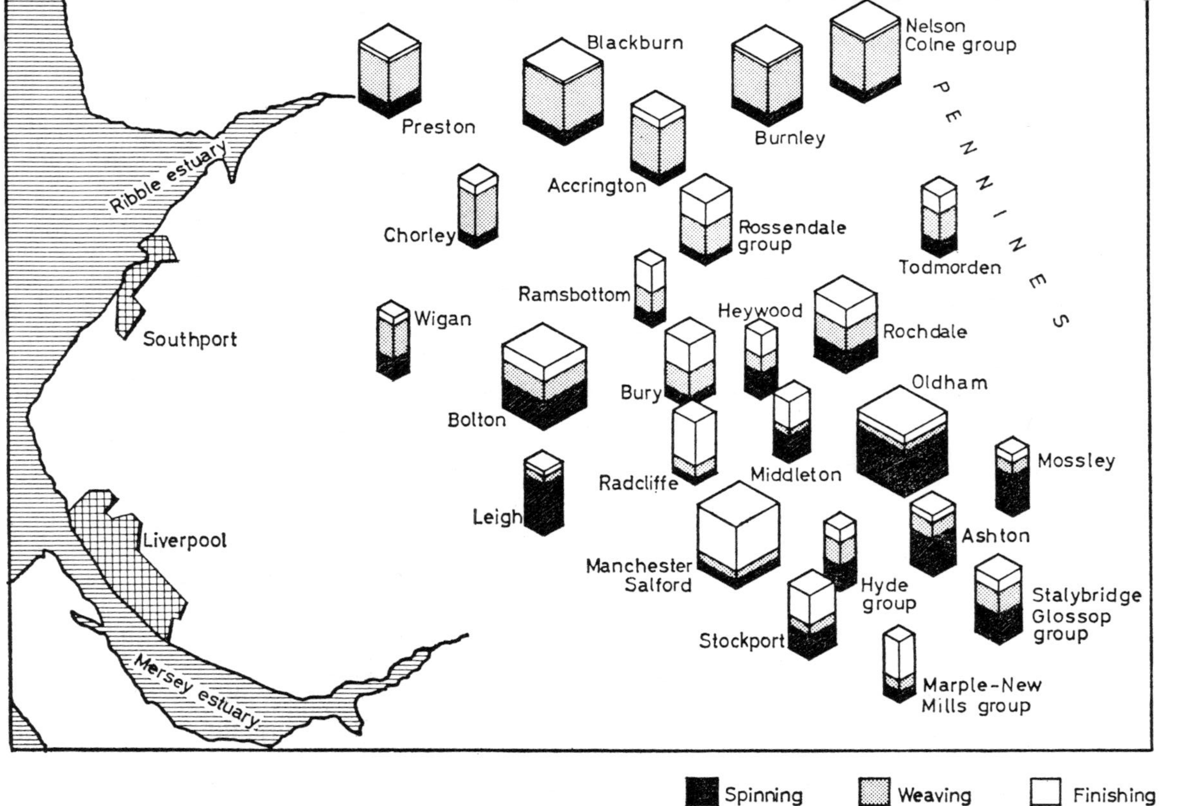

Fig 24. Distribution of the 'Lancashire' textile industry, *c* 1906. The concentration of spinning in the South (particularly in Oldham and Bolton) and of weaving in the North is a most striking feature

Difficulties of communication during the nineteenth century had favoured the development of local machinery makers, and naturally those in the Oldham area tended to specialise in machinery for coarse and medium count spinning, while those in the Bolton area specialised in machinery for the finer numbers. It is, of course, much more difficult to spin fine yarns, and long after self-actors had become usual in other sections of the trade the fine spinners of Bolton still favoured the hand mule. So the Bolton machinery makers continued to develop the hand mule, bringing it to a remarkable pitch of sensitivity. Their ultimate masterpiece may well qualify as the most complex, and most highly refined, manually controlled tool which has yet been, or will ever be, mass produced. Spencer summarised the position in 1880:

> For spinning the finest counts of yarn the hand mule has been brought to great perfection; all its operations being now automatic, or nearly so. The 'spinner', as he is called, has only to supply the little power required to control some of the motions. This he is able to do easily, even when the mules are large; but it requires very close attention on his part, coupled with an extremely sensitive touch, which can only be acquired by long practice. To back-off, wind, and lift the faller at the termination of the inward run of the carriage, in first class style, demands great skill on the part of the operator.
>
> Men of first class ability as spinners become scarcer year by year; and the necessity of reducing the cost of spinning has called special attention to the question of making this mule entirely automatic. During the last 25 years many patents have been taken out, and many schemes have been tried, but the general results have been very unsatisfactory. The methods were generally of too provisional a character.

Spencer's strictures concerning the development of self-actors for fine counts were not without substance although 'very unsatisfactory' was perhaps too strong a comment. True, they had not been completely successful but a great deal of headway nevertheless had been made and during the next twenty years very satisfactory self-actors for the finest yarns were developed on the principles he condemned. It is not difficult to appreciate his point that 'methods were generally of too provisional a character'. He meant that a

Bolton spinner would usually prefer to add successive devices to remedy a basic mechanism, where he, an Oldham machinery maker, would strive instead to evolve an ideal basic mechanism. Spencer, of course, was advocating the very philosophy by which Roberts had succeeded in making a self-actor when almost half a century of 'methods of too provisional a character' had failed.

In the event Spencer was proved wrong. Self-actors in the Bolton style became widely used for spinning the finest yarns and, although they made considerable demands on the skill of both overlookers and minders, they were completely self-acting and eventually almost entirely displaced hand mules. Spencer's company, Platt Bros, also had some success as makers of mules for fine yarns but their Special Fine mule was something of a compromise. It had many of the features of the typical Oldham mule, including cam-shaft changes, but these were supplemented by a whole host of additional motions in true Bolton style. (In fact, although it had cam-shaft changes, it was not on the usual system. It used a three-position cam-shaft and in that sense it had much in common with the Bolton mules which used a three-position long lever.) Considering the difficulties normally encountered when 'playing away', it is to Platts' credit that their mule found even limited acceptance among the fine spinners of Bolton: but it must be conceded that the home team won. Right up to the time when the manufacture of cotton mules ceased the Bolton machinery makers, in particular Richard Threlfall and Messrs Dobson & Barlow, continued to dominate the market for fine spinning mules. An example of a fine mule headstock of the Bolton style is shown on page 134.

How did the complex, aristocratic Bolton-style mule differ from its simple plebeian counterpart? Broadly the differences met special requirements in three distinct categories: there were important modifications in the drafting rollers, in motions concerned with the smoothness of action of the machine, and in motions concerned with the precision of operation.

A spinner from another district would be most struck, if not actually confounded, by the differences in the arrangement of drafting rollers. Thomas Thornley, a recent immigrant to Bolton in 1899, wrote:

> In some districts in England a fluker rod is absolutely unknown, and if given a trial would be utterly condemned. On the other hand, in the Bolton district it appears to be much preferred.

The essential difference in the arrangement can be seen by comparing the schematic diagram of the Bolton system, Fig 25, with the Oldham system seen in Fig 11. The literature of the period, which is largely descriptive, only speculates on the need for the differences, and it can be reasonably assumed that the Oldham and Bolton systems were separately developed by empirical methods. More recently, scientific investigation of the mechanism of roller drafting has greatly clarified the picture and shown that the Bolton system was by far the more highly developed. Both were three-line systems: but whereas in the Oldham system all three lines of rollers were loaded by a saddle-and-lever system, only the front (ie the delivery) roller was additionally loaded in Bolton. The other two lines gripped the roving only by virtue of their own weight.

Another difference was that the flannel-covered clearer rollers which ran in contact with the fluted iron bottom roller in the Oldham system were not used in Bolton. Instead the fluker rod, a rotating iron shaft mounted below the rollers, served to collect waste roving when an end was broken, but played no part in keeping the surface of the iron roller clean. Because the form of weight hook used to load the front rollers in the Bolton system prevented the Oldham type of flannel-covered underclearer being used, it has sometimes been suggested that this was the reason for the use of the fluker rod in Bolton. This is too facile an explanation. If flannel-covered underclearers had really been needed it would have been a simple enough matter to devise a form of weight hook which would permit their use. On balance the fluker rod must have been more suited to Bolton requirements. The Oldham sticks had two functions. The first was to remove short fibres or fly which might otherwise cling to the front roller. The second was to take up the roving issuing from the roller when an end was broken, so that it neither formed a roller lap nor made bad work by becoming attached to adjacent ends. Now the cottons used in Bolton were generally long, fine growths from which all short fibre and fly had been combed in an earlier process. Thus the

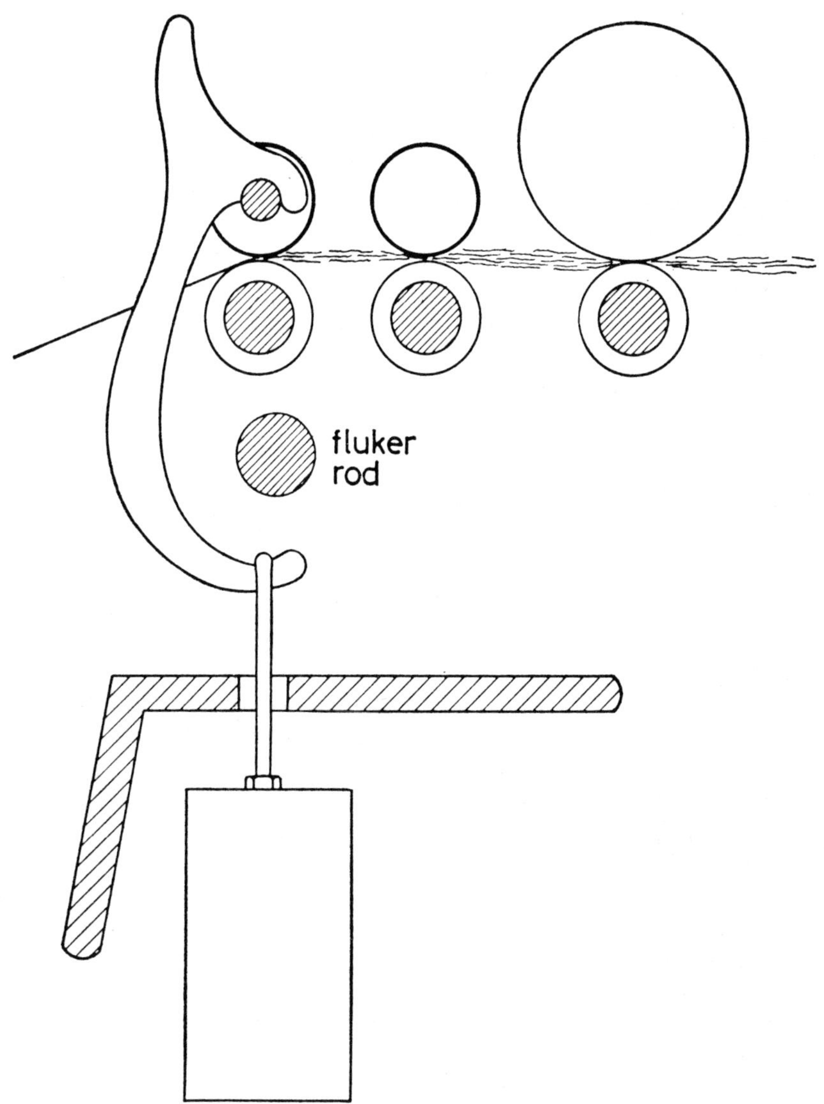

Fig 25. Bolton style drafting rollers. As in the Oldham system the three lower rollers are fluted, made of iron and are positively driven. The important difference is that only the front roller of the upper three was leather covered and loaded. The other two were of polished iron and had no loading except their own weight

Bolton spinner had no need of an underclearer for its first function. The fluker rod performed the second function very adequately, without the frequent cleaning which sticks needed, and moreover was much cheaper to install and maintain.

A third feature of the Bolton style was the use of single-end bosses. It was explained in an earlier chapter that top rollers were made in pairs, two leather-covered bosses being attached to, or running freely on, a common mandrel. For somewhat complex reasons, the degree of accuracy with which the front rollers of a drafting system must be made and covered increases as the draft ratio is increased. It was quite convenient to spin Oldham counts with draft ratios of the order of five to seven: but for the fine numbers spun in Bolton very much higher ratios were needed. For Oldham conditions long bosses, each controlling two, three or even four ends (shown on page 133), were satisfactory: but to achieve the accuracy needed for the high draft ratios of Bolton it was necessary to limit the length of the bosses, and it was only possible to run with one end to each boss (as shown on page 152).

Thus the Bolton-style mule looked odd to a spinner from other parts. The greatly increased number of roller bosses, the prominent weight hook projecting between each pair of ends and the complete absence of underclearers would immediately confuse him. When, as a friendly visitor, he attempted to piece a broken end he would be at a complete loss. At home he might well be able to piece two adjacent ends simultaneously with consummate ease but here things were very different. After barking his knuckles on the protruding weight hook, he would realise that it was necessary to hold the yarn in a different way and to approach the roller nip with a markedly different action. After observing how the natives did it he would, perhaps, try again, only to find that the lack of an underclearer called for a subtly different technique in the actual piecing. Ruefully he would admit that the skill he had so painstakingly acquired as a little piecer was of no use to him in this alien land.

Although puzzled by the drafting roller arrangements, the visitor would be reassured on walking through the mule gate to the headstock, where he would recognise the main features of the self-actor.

The quadrant, with its nosing motion and strapping motion, and the drives to the spindles, rollers and carriage were little changed. He would, however, be surprised by the absence of a cam-shaft and by the use of a belt drive in place of the usual band drive for backing-off and taking up the mule.

The crisp, almost explosive way in which a cam-shaft made the changes would have delighted the most exacting drill sergeant, and this sort of action completely met the needs of coarse-yarn spinners determined to get the maximum number of draws in each hour. For Bolton yarns, however, a gentler approach was needed and this was achieved by direct action from the long lever without any powered assistance.

The long lever, a horizontal bar lying along the headstock side and pivoted at its mid-point, had been a common feature before Roberts introduced the cam-shaft. In the simplest form an arrangement of studs and inclines merely tilted the lever as the carriage reached the end of the outward run and returned it to its original position on completion of the inward run. Roberts used a lever of this sort to trigger the engagement of the friction clutch by which powered changes were made, and a simple long lever was always used for this purpose on cam-shaft mules.

Although they applied many other features of the Roberts self-actor (including the winding quadrant) to their hand mules, the fine spinners of Bolton rejected the powered cam-shaft and instead continued development of the long-lever method of making the changes. William Slater and Robert Halliwell of Bolton, in co-operation with Benjamin Dobson of Messrs Dobson & Barlow, took a leading part in this development. Their patent of 1864 described a three-position system of long-lever actuation which soon became established as a common feature of self-actors for fine counts.

The two leading makers of fine mules, Richard Threlfall and Messrs Dobson & Barlow, each had their own preferred forms of long-lever mechanism. A common feature was that the movements of the lever were not, in general, made directly by movement of the carriage. Rather they were triggered when the carriage, or some other working element, reached a precisely determined position after a spring had been charged, or an actuating lever raised, by an earlier movement. Generally the long lever itself had three positions—spinning, backing-off and taking up—and safety interlocks were provided to prevent damage from dual engagement.

An example of one of the more highly developed arrangements is shown in Figs 26 and 27. This was used on the Threlfall Special Mule which had a very high reputation for spinning the finest yarns. The makers' catalogue of 1905 proudly listed 'A few of the Firms using the Threlfall Special Mule'. It included more than seventy firms in seven countries (including Russia and America), with a total of 2,766,800 spindles. Heading the list was William Heaton & Sons, of Bolton, with 263,420 spindles in a single firm. The two figures show the complex mechanism from opposite sides of the headstock. The components seen in Fig 26 are mainly concerned with drawing-out, jacking, twisting at the head and backing-off. Fig 27 shows the parts which controlled taking up and the initiation of drawing-out.

The ingenuity of form of the secondary levers, catches and pendants used is reminiscent of the devices used by clockmakers to actuate chimes and gongs in sequence, and the action too had much in common with that of well-ordered clockwork. Where the common self-actor went through its changes in the brisk, staccato manner of a well-drilled guardsman on the barrack square, the long-lever mule proceeded in the calm unhurried fashion of a master craftsman. This took a little longer of course: but with fine yarns requiring so many more turns of twist the whole cycle of operations was very much more protracted, and the saving of a little time in the changes was of relatively minor importance.

The same philosophy was applied to the initiation of all the actions. Although conical friction clutches were used for backing-off they were engaged slowly to ensure smoothness at the expense of speed. The same end was sought in taking up. Scroll shafts similar to those on other mules were used, but the drive was by a flat belt rather than by the more positive rope and V-groove system. Dobson & Barlow had a cone clutch in the drive to the scroll shaft but arranged that the driving belt, which also drove the backing-off frictions, was only partially on the fast pulley at the time of engagement of the clutch. Richard Threlfall ensured a

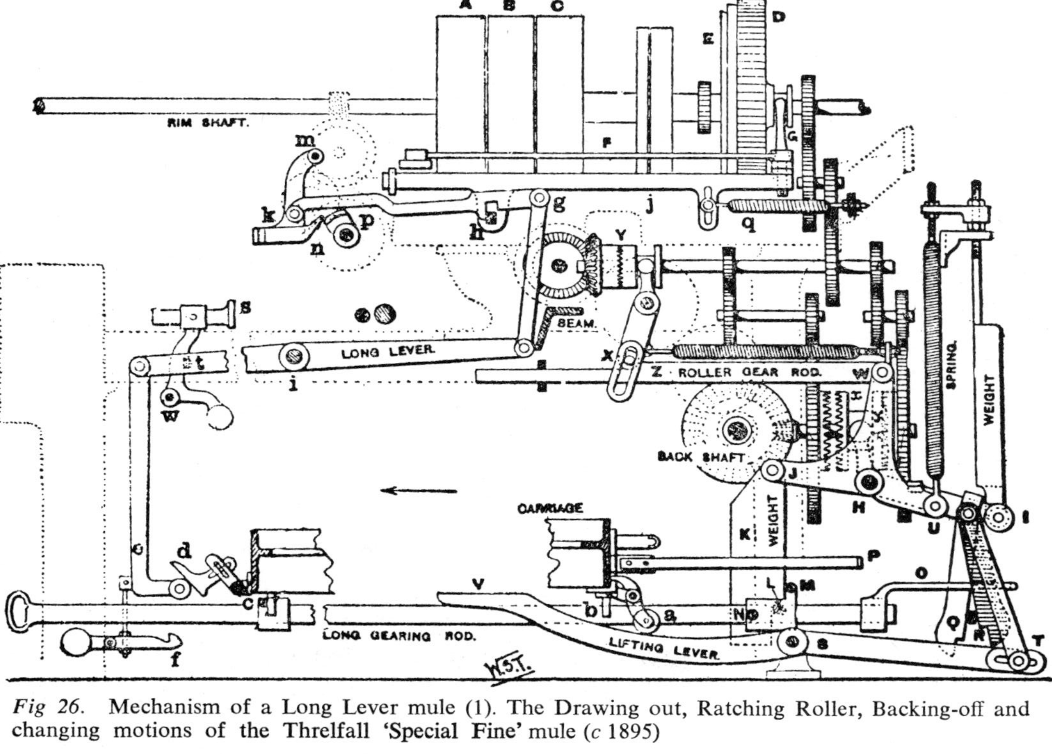

Fig 26. Mechanism of a Long Lever mule (1). The Drawing out, Ratching Roller, Backing-off and changing motions of the Threlfall 'Special Fine' mule (*c* 1895)

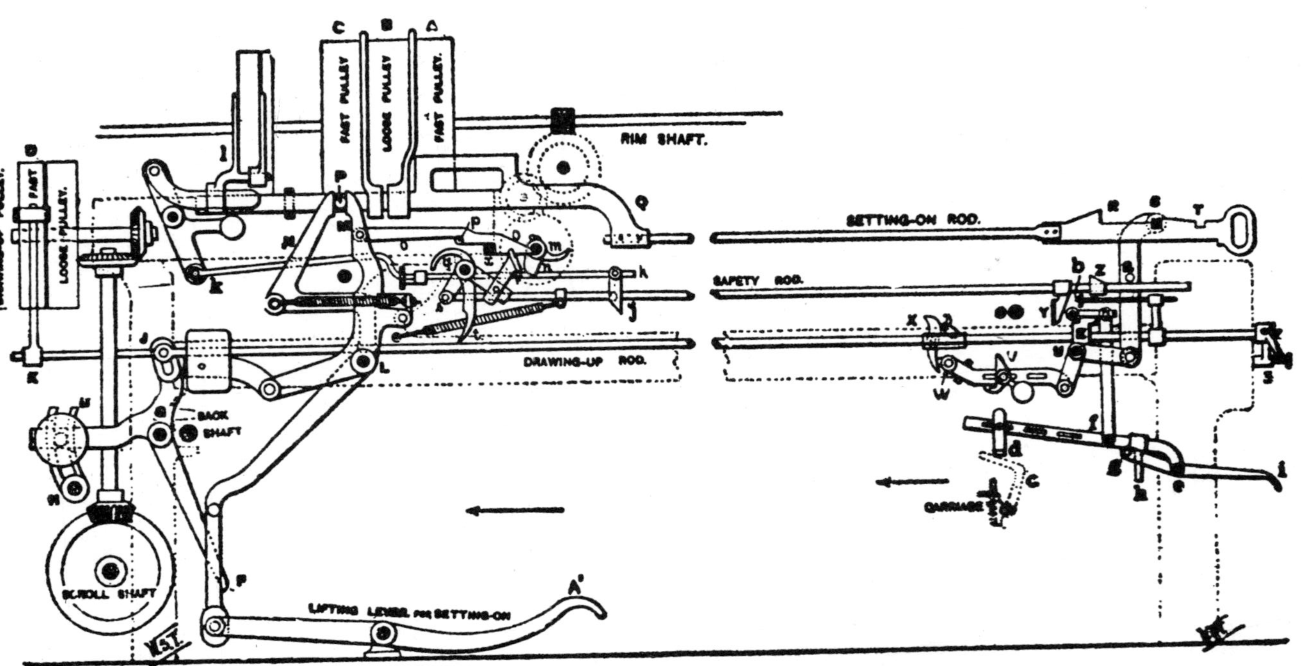

Fig 27. Mechanism of a Long Lever mule (2). The Setting-on and Drawing-up motions of Threlfall's 'Special Fine' mule

smooth start to the inward run by dispensing with the clutch and using instead the relatively gentle action of a flat belt moved from a loose to a fast pulley.

The driving of the rim shaft was also complicated by the desire for smoothness and two principal elaborations were used. To ensure a smooth start at the commencement of spinning the snicking motion, a device rather like the hastening motion, was developed. The ordinary hastening motion, which moved the main down strap partially onto the fast pulley of the rim shaft just before the cam-shaft change, and thus began to accelerate the rim shaft and spindles in anticipation of the commencement of the draw, was a rather crude device which has already been discussed in Chapter 6. The snicking motion acted much more gently by using a separate, and much lighter belt, running at a slower speed. The arrangement used by Messrs Dobson & Barlow is shown in Fig 28.

Pulleys A and D were fixed to the rim shaft and pulleys B and C were free. In the illustration the parts are shown in the position they occupied immediately before the end of the inward run. Although the belts are not shown it is clear that the main down strap would be on loose pulley C and the snicking strap on loose pulley B. As the stud J, mounted on the carriage, ran under the incline K it would lift the lever L and release the latch N. Spring S would then cause the bar P, carrying strap fork Q to move to the left and lead the snicking strap onto its fast pulley. This action would relatively gently accelerate the rim shaft and spindles a second or so before actuation of the long lever moved the strap fork H to the right and the main down strap onto its fast pulley. As this occurred the main strap-fork arm would contact the stud R to return the snicking strap to its loose pulley and re-engage the latch N. In an installation described by Thornley the pulley and countershaft arrangement would have given a rim-shaft speed of 140 rpm against a speed with the main down strap fully engaged of 700 rpm. This lower speed, together with the much lighter belt used for snicking, would give a much smoother start than was possible when only the main down strap was used.

The second elaboration of the rim-shaft drive of Special Fine mules was the use of double-speed motions. These were not double speed in the sense that the speed was increased by a factor of two but double in the sense that two speeds were used. With this convention it would have been logical to call such a mule, also fitted with a snicking motion, a triple-speed mule. For successful spinning of fine yarns it was necessary to put only a fraction of the total final twist (sometimes only two-thirds) into the yarn during the draw. The rollers were then stopped a little before the end of the outward run and the yarn was jacked or ratched to pull out any soft thin places by the last few inches of carriage movement. When this was completed the spindles continued 'twisting at the head' to put in the remaining turns of twist needed. During this supplementary twisting the rollers were turned to deliver a little extra roving to relieve the tension being generated in the yarn by continued twisting.

Double-speed motions were introduced when it was found that a very much higher spindle speed could be used while twisting at the head than was satisfactory during the draw. Commonly the increase in speed was of the order of one-third. Typically the increase would be from about 6,000 rpm during the draw to about 8,000 rpm at the head, although Thornley records seeing mules spinning 80's twist with a speed during draw of 7,500 rpm and at the head of 11,500 rpm.

In the early days of double-speed working the two speeds were obtained by varying the speed of the countershaft. This had the great advantage that it did not involve any alteration of the mule itself. A common arrangement was to run two driving belts, instead of the usual one, from the line shaft to the countershaft. Each belt had its own set of one fast and two loose pulleys. A linked strap-fork mechanism enabled either belt to be on a fast pulley or both belts to be on loose pulleys, but prevented both belts being simultaneously on fast pulleys. The pulley ratios were, of course, such as to give the two rim-shaft speeds desired.

This system had merit because it could be used with existing single-speed mules. However, it was clumsy and by no means cheap because of the much larger and heavier counter-shaft assembly needed, and the cost of maintaining two expensive main driving belts. It was natural, therefore, that interest was aroused in the idea of providing two-speed devices within the mule itself. The

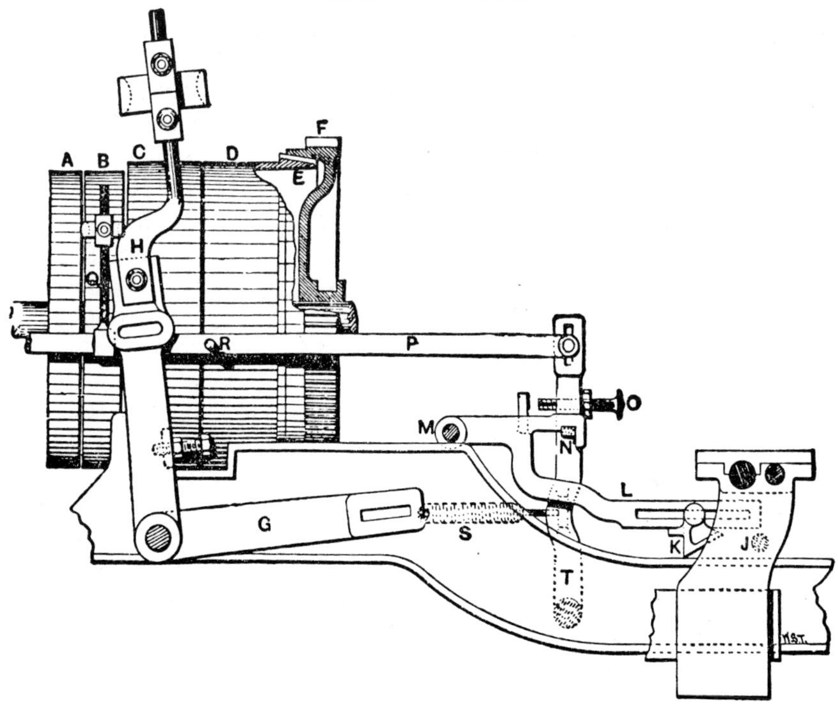

Fig 28. Snicking motion of the type fitted by Messrs Dobson and Barlow

firm of Richard Threlfall was particularly prolific in this field and for many years offered double-speed headstocks working on two different principles.

The simpler of these used toothed gearing to give the higher speed. Only a single main downstrap was needed with one loose pulley mounted between two fast pulleys. One of the fast pulleys was secured directly to the rim shaft and was used to give the standard speed during the draw in the ordinary way. The other was not a fast pulley in the usual sense. It was free on the rim shaft but coupled to it through a gear train, rather in the fashion of a back-geared lathe headstock. Whereas the lathe back-gearing gave a substantial speed reduction, however, the gearing in this case was such as to give a speed increase of about one-third. The action was very simple. During the outward run the down belt was on the true fast pulley driving at standard speed. On completion of the draw the belt was moved smartly across the loose pulley onto the geared fast pulley to give a higher spindle speed for the period of twisting at the head.

On Threlfall's Special Fine mule a rather more complex device was used. The arrangement is shown in Fig 29. The rim shaft was in two parts extending from the back to the front of the headstock. The rim band passed round a large V-grooved pulley on the front rim shaft and also round a smaller pulley on the back rim shaft. As on the geared double-speed mule, there were three pulleys for the main down belt, one loose and two fast. With the belt on the back fast pulley C, the rim band and spindles were driven at normal speed by the small rim pulley at the back of the headstock. For twisting at the head the belt was moved to the front pulley, which was secured to the front rim shaft, so that the rim band and spindles were driven at a higher speed by the larger front rim pulley. This was a relatively difficult mechanical arrangement in that it involved a two-piece, long rim shaft. Consequently there were problems of bearing alignment and the exceptionally long rim band followed an even more complex path than usual. In addition it was found necessary to provide a brake mechanism to help stop the front rim shaft during backing-off (the back rim shaft was stopped in the usual way by the backing-off friction). Despite these difficulties it was an extremely successful type of double-speed motion. It made it possible to vary the two speeds independently with little trouble and expense, and it worked smoothly and quietly (the geared double-speed mules were rather noisy).

The third and final category of special features found on fine spinning mules is that of motions concerned with the precision of operation. Hand-mule spinning of very fine yarns called for the greatest skill and precision in the co-ordination of reverse spindle rotation and faller depression during backing-off, and of forward spindle rotation and faller lifting during laying-on. The motions used on an ordinary self-actor were not good enough, and special motions were developed.

The usual way in which the faller was brought down during

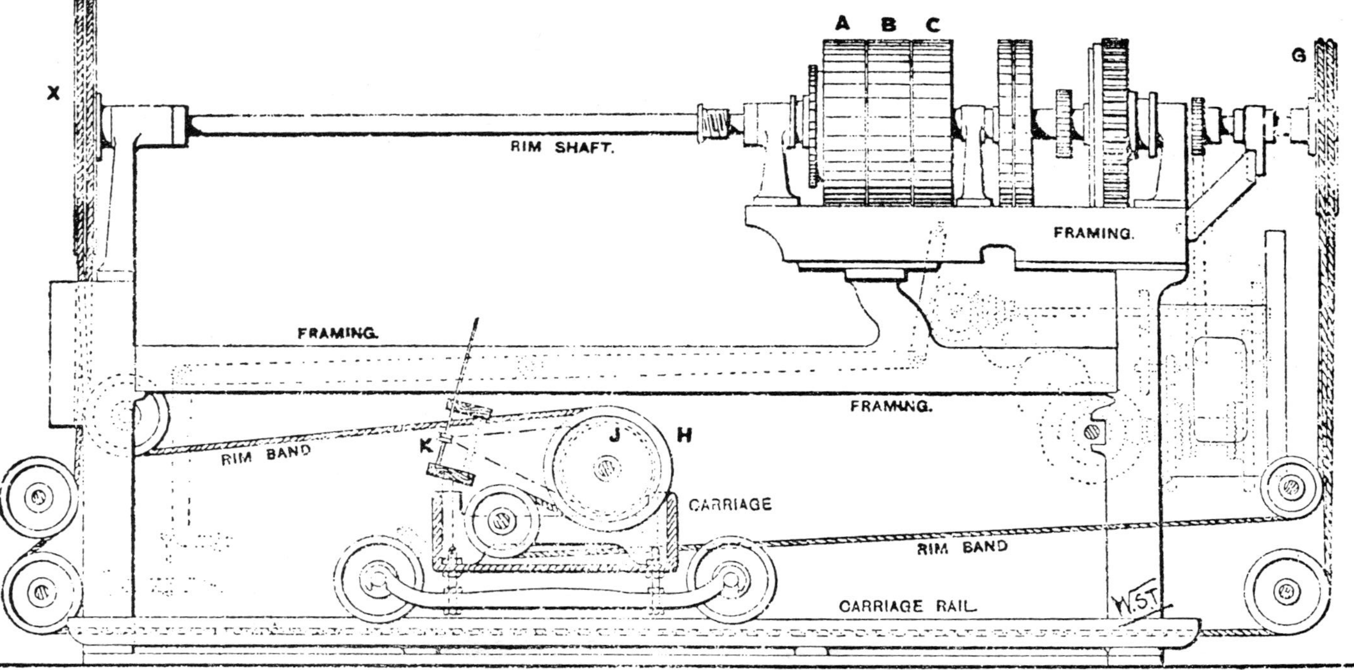

Fig 29. The 'double speed' arrangement used on later Threlfall 'Special Fine' mules. It was double speed in the sense that it gave two spindle speeds related by the ratio of the diameters of the two rim pulleys, G and X

backing-off was described in Chapter 5. Reverse rotation of the tin roller caused a pawl to engage and rotate a ratchet which mounted freely on the tin roller shaft. A drum attached to the ratchet wheel wound up a chain connected to a sector on the faller shaft and thus depressed the faller against the pull of a spring.

This mechanism, shown in Fig 19 (page 94) was basically sound in that it ensured that the rate of faller depression was directly related to the rate at which the coils of yarn were freed from the spindle blade. Its weakness was that on completion of spinning the faller was at least 1 in above the yarn, and it was therefore necessary to depress the faller at a rate higher than that at which the spindle blade was being cleared in order that the faller wire could overtake the yarn during backing-off. This expedient was not entirely satisfactory even for coarse yarn because the distance (or time) during which the overtaking had to be done changed as cop formation proceeded. Immediately after doffing, about 6 in of spindle blade would be stripped and the faller would be depressed approximately 7 in during backing-off. Before doffing, with a full cop on the spindles, only 1 in of spindle blade was to be stripped, but the faller had to be depressed at least 2 in.

The use of a variable-diameter chain drum (a snail or scroll) helped, but the major correction for the disparity was obtained by the use of backing-off chain-tightening motions. These depended on the size of the snail being such that the mean rate of faller depression was always greater than the real need. Means were provided by which the backing-off chain was slack at the beginning of backing-off, and the amount of slackness was varied either manually or automatically. Thus the commencement of actual faller depression was delayed just sufficiently to enable the faller to overtake and contact the yarn on the instant of completion of backing-off.

This rather crude expedient was widely used but left much to be desired. Thornley wrote:

> Although something can be said in favour of this practice, we are by no means inclined to admit that it is the best method of remedying the coil. By slackening the chain we delay the commencement of the downward movement, but when it does start

Page 133: (left) Spinning on late period self-actors. These are Oldham-style mules, and from the grouping of threads it can be seen that there are four ends to a boss; (right) Self-actor headstock viewed from behind. (The domed device projecting from the rim pulley is a dynamometer fitted for research purposes, not a normal fitment)

Page 134: (above) Threlfall's 'Special Fine' mule, c 1895; (below) A Whitely woollen mule, c 1900

> it is made with just the same speed as before, and when the threads are reached they are struck too savagely by the wire.

He expressed a preference for arrangements by which the use of an intermediate differential drum, placed between the snail and the faller shaft sector, increased the angle turned by the snail. This increased angle of rotation is then used to get a greater speed range from beginning to end of the snail motion and hence a closer approximation to the real requirement.

The only way in which the basic difficulty could be completely overcome was by depressing the faller into contact with the yarn before starting to back-off. This was the way in which hand-mule spinners worked and although it could not be done directly by the usual backing-off mechanism of the self-actor, it was not difficult to achieve by means of a supplementary motion. A particularly simple form of such a motion was that fitted to the special fine spinning mules made by Platt Bros. As the carriage approached the end of the outward run the outer end of an arm fixed to the faller shaft came into contact with a fixed incline mounted on the headstock frame. During the last few inches of carriage movement the end of the arm ran up the incline and turned the faller shaft to depress the faller wire to within about $\frac{1}{8}$ in of the yarn sheet.[1] This required accurate setting of the faller wire along its whole length, for if the wire had touched the yarn sheet anywhere the ends there would have been broken during twisting at the head. Used in conjunction with a differential chain drum and a conventional backing-off chain-tightening motion, the arrangement worked very well indeed.

An almost equally simple arrangement used by Richard Threlfall acted through the backing-off chain itself in a way which dispensed with the need for a chain-tightening motion. This too worked well, and it was surprising that a motion so simple to apply and so sound in its basic approach to the solution of a problem always present,

[1] The reader not familiar with mule-spinning practice might wonder why the faller was not kept in this position throughout the draw. The answer is that it was necessary to have the faller wire at least 1 in above the yarn sheet to permit an operative to get finger and thumb to the spindle tip when picking up a broken end for piecing.

whatever count was being spun, was not applied universally to all self-actors.

The lifting of the winding faller for laying-on also presented problems for the fine-spinning self-actor. On a hand mule the spinner would allow the mule to let-in before raising the faller and he would then take care to raise the faller at a speed so related to the acceleration of the spindles as to lay the coils of yarn on the spindle blade at the pitch angle he deemed to be ideal. The ordinary self-actor offered but little refinement. The boot leg, a pendent strut by which the faller was held in the winding position, was merely unlatched from the copping-lever stud by striking the unlocking bracket at the termination of the inward run (see Chapter 5 and Fig 19). Unlatching the boot leg allowed the faller to rise to its working position in response to the pull of springs or weights. This was a dynamic action which, at the best, could lay-on the coils in a near-perfect helix. When, due perhaps to variations in the engine speed, the carriage let-in rather slowly, the unlatching would occur a little early. The faller would rise before the spindles were accelerated, the laying-on would then be done in a more open helix and snarls would be formed by the surplus yarn. Conversely, a rise in engine speed would result in relatively late raising of thc faller, a closer-pitched helix and breakage or nicking of the yarn. Normally the minder would take care of speed variations by tightening or slackening the check scroll band, and on coarse or medium counts he was able to get by. On finer counts, however, it was found necessary to control the lifting of the winding faller more precisely.

A device which ensured more consistent timing of the unlatching of the boot leg was a simple trigger mechanism rather like that used to actuate the long lever of a Bolton mule. Instead of the usual fixed unlocking bracket, which relied on the momentum of the carriage to dislodge the boot leg, a form of triggered hammer was used. The vertical arm of a bell crank lever carried the unlocking bracket and the horizontal arm was heavily weighted. At some convenient time in the mule cycle the weighted arm was raised and supported by a catch. The last inch or so of movement of the carriage triggered the catch. The weight arm fell, gathering sufficient momentum for the moving unlocking bracket to dislodge the boot leg from the copping-lever stud by a clean blow. It was a simple and effective device which was used in various forms. A popular variant had a sliding unlocking bracket actuated by a spring.

Although it gave more precise timing of the rise of the faller than the usual arrangement did, the triggered unlocking bracket alone did not give good enough laying-on for the finest yarns. An action more closely imitating that of the hand-mule spinner was needed, and this was provided by one or other of a number of motions which positively related the rate of lift of the winding faller to the speed of rotation of the spindles. Platt Bros' motion was a rather elaborate one which used two special volute gear sectors. One sector was keyed to the faller shaft and the other was geared to the tin-roller shaft during backing-off. This arrangement required an extremely complex clutch engagement and disengagement mechanism. A description of the mechanism written by Eli Spencer conveys the impression that Platt Bros gloried in its sheer complexity. Referring to the means by which the clutch was disengaged, he wrote:

> . . . its wedge action draws the friction cones asunder and thus severs the motion from the tin-roller to the faller. This action is a very beautiful one.

A much simpler embodiment of the same principle was used by Richard Threlfall. This used the existing backing-off chain instead of the special gear sectors used by Platts. The coupling of the backing-off snail to the tin roller was through the same free wheel, or click, unit by which the faller was drawn down during backing-off. This relatively simple motion had the great merit that the laying-on helix exactly matched the backing-off action. Again one is puzzled by the fact that such a simple yet sound device was not universally applied. Certainly it was not, and only mules for the very finest counts fitted any form of faller raising motion.

Complementary to these devices for the more precise control of the winding faller, during backing-off and laying-on, were a number of counterfaller easing motions. The simplest of them were simply floor-mounted inclines which supported some of the counterfaller weighting levers when the carriage was fully in or out. These were readily adjustable and were quite widely used over the whole range of counts. For fine spinning more elaborate mechanisms were developed with the object of relating the load on the counterfaller to the position of the winding faller. A common arrangement was for a spring force to be applied in opposition to the counterfaller weights at the beginning of the upward movement of the counterfaller during backing-off. By this means the first contact of the wire and the yarn sheet was made very gently indeed yet without reducing the weight applied from the commencement of winding.

This third category of special features on fine spinning mules should include the short copping rail, already referred to in Chapter 5. Why the short rail was popular in Bolton remains something of a mystery. The claim that it was convenient when changing the length of draw (a much shorter draw, perhaps only 50 in against the more usual 64 in, was used when spinning exceptionally fine yarns) is unconvincing. A shortening of the draw could be satisfactorily accommodated merely by an inward movement of the complete rail and plates assembly, to keep the apex of the rail in the same proportional position relative to the draw, together with a resetting of the plates slightly to increase the rail gradients. This could be done quite easily with either system: but, in fact, by far the greater proportion of mules fitted with short rails were operated for their whole life without ever having the length of draw changed, and ready adjustment of draw length was never an important requirement. Another claim was that the short rail (roughly one-quarter of the length of the usual fixed rail) was much more rigid and thereby gave more precise cop formation. This too is doubtful. There is no evidence that the conventional rail lacked sufficient rigidity, and also the wear of the guides used to locate the movement of the short rail was likely to be at least as prejudicial to the most precise copping. Perhaps both systems were equally good and it was only by chance that the long rail came to be used in Oldham and the short rail in Bolton.

There was, however, one copping feature of real significance sometimes found on fine mules. This was the use of a differently proportioned rail giving more nearly equal duration of rise and fall than was usual. The need for this arose from the fact that many fine yarns were not used directly in the shuttle but were first doubled to make a two-fold yarn. During the doubling process it was sometimes more convenient to allow the cops to rotate on a pointed skewer rather than have them fixed and withdraw the yarn over-end as in the shuttle. The ordinary cop, although ideal for over-end unwinding, gave trouble in this situation because of the rapid acceleration needed when unwinding the binding coils (the 'quick-down' layer wound during the first 10 to 12 in of the inward run). In conjunction with an increased length of front incline (up to 18 or 20 in) modification of the quadrant geometry was used further to increase the length of yarn wound in the downward helix.

8

The Woollen Mule

ALTHOUGH in principle the mule could be used to spin all textile fibres, in practice its complete dominance was restricted to cottons and woollens. It was little used for flax, jute or silk and had only a limited vogue for fine worsteds. That it made no impact in the flax, jute or silk trades is probably because the water frame, the throstle and the ring frame was each in turn found to be entirely adequate for these relatively easily spun fibres. As the mule was a very much more complex, yet slightly less productive, machine it had no place in these industries. With regard to worsteds the situation is less clear. Mule-spun worsted yarns were found to be superior to their throstle or ring-spun counterparts and many worsted mules were installed and operated, particularly in France, during the second half of the nineteenth century. The mules used were very like cotton mules except that the drafting rollers, quite naturally, were made much larger in diameter to suit the longer staple length of worsted wools.

In Britain the cap frame came to be preferred to the mule for spinning fine worsteds (the throstle and ring frame were quickly accepted for coarser worsteds, on the grounds that the twist was soft, regular and even and a minimum of strain was involved in winding). In France, however, a different system of preparatory drafting was developed and excellent yarns were produced on mules. The French developments were completely successful and, as a result, the British worsted industry suffered severe competition from imports of mule-spun French and Belgian yarns: their Continental rivals were able to produce better-quality yarns with less labour and from cheaper wools than could the British worsted spinner.

Why, in the face of this situation, the mule was not widely used for worsted is something of a mystery. It cannot be ascribed to geographical difficulties, for the centre of the West Riding worsted industry was only twenty-five miles from the centre of the Lancashire cotton industry. Perhaps the traditional rivalry between the counties, born of the Wars of the Roses, was the root of the difficulty: the White Rose reluctant to accept an innovation originated by the Red Rose faction?

Woollen spinners, however, had no such scruples. First the hand mule and later the self-actor were taken and enthusiastically adapted to meet the special requirements of woollen spinning. Indeed, they were so successful that today the last stronghold of mule spinning is the woollen industry, and although the last cotton mules were built more than forty years ago a few woollen mules are still being made.

Cotton and worsted yarns have a great deal in common, but woollens are radically different in structure. For cotton and worsted spinning the fibres are first made straight and parallel by a series of preparatory processes. The resulting yarns are lean and lustrous and almost entirely dependent on twist for their cohesion. Woollen yarns, in contrast, are spun directly from the carded wool without any preparatory drawing or combing processes and, in consequence, there is a great deal of entanglement of the fibres. Because of this entanglement very little twist is needed and the finished yarns are relatively soft and full, but lack lustre.

For many years after the invention of the mule, woollen yarns continued to be spun on the simple jenny. This was natural enough as the special feature of the mule, the use of drafting rollers, offered no advantage to the woollen spinner. These machines had no rollers at all and used fixed spindles and creel in conjunction with a moving clove or clasp. The example illustrated on page 18 is a typical woollen jenny and was in regular use in Dobcross, Yorkshire until 1916.

Although the woollen spinner had no need of drafting rollers he quickly appreciated the value of the degree of automation embodied in the Roberts self-actor. Within a few years of the establishment of the new machine for cotton spinning, a modified version suitable for woollen spinning became available. It might have been better had the makers set out to construct a machine which was essentially a jenny yet incorporating the self-acting principles of the new mule. In the event they chose to take the already highly developed mule and adapt it to work as a jenny. Thus, although the machine which became so widely used in the industry was (and is still) known as the woollen mule, it is not a true mule. It is really a self-acting jenny.

At first it was a simplified version of the cotton self-actor with just one pair of gripping rollers, to act as the clove of a jenny, in place of the more usual set of three pairs of drafting rollers. Early machines were fed from individual bobbins or cops of roving: but it later became the practice to have multiple-end bobbins, each containing from twenty to sixty rovings. These were prepared directly from the card by condensing apparatus which first split the card web into the requisite number of ribbons and then formed these ribbons of web into roving by rubbing them between transversely oscillating moving aprons. With this system of operation the labour costs in making woollen yarns were very low indeed, and there was the added advantage that the shortest fibres, which would have been lost in conventional drafting, were rubbed into the yarn and retained.

The ability to retain short fibres also made the system ideal for the spinning of waste cotton containing much damaged fibre. After the introduction of the comber for fine cottons in 1851, a trade in the spinning of woollen-type yarns from cotton comber waste sprang up in Lancashire. By lucky chance this development occurred at a time when the revolving flat card was beginning to replace the roller and clearer card in Lancashire, and the practice of double or tandem carding was being superseded by single carding plus combing. In consequence a great many roller and clearer cards became surplus to requirements, enabling the new trade to be set up using second-hand roller and clearer cards fitted with roving condensers of the woollen pattern.

Condenser cotton spinning, as it came to be known, was soon firmly established and the yarns were in great demand for cotton blankets, raised sheets and winceyettes. As in woollen spinning no roller drafting was needed, and modified cotton self-actor mules were found to be ideal for the spinning of these soft full yarns. Woollen spinning and condenser cotton spinning had very much in common that was distinct from ordinary cotton spinning, and over the years special mules were developed to meet these common needs. In describing the machine which was evolved (it is referred to below as the woollen mule) it should be stressed that it was not a true mule but a self-acting jenny and its use was not confined to the spinning of woollens. It was equally widely used for spinning cotton waste.

In addition to having only one pair of gripping rollers, the early woollen mules were further simplified by the omission of many of the motions commonly found on cotton mules. This may well have been merely the result of real financial stringency, although there was also the consideration that some of the motions omitted were less important when spinning coarse yarns (the common range of woollen mule counts was equivalent to 2's to 16's cotton count). The need for a nosing motion, for example, was greatly reduced by the use of much thicker spindles, which were, in fact, preferable when spinning soft thick yarn. The strapping motion, too, was often omitted and this could be justified on two counts. Firstly the time spent in forming the cop bottom with coarse yarns was so short that it was not too onerous for the minder to have to be in close attendance on the mule during this period. This was probably an important consideration, because when spinning fine yarns, cop-bottom formation could take six, eight or even ten hours: but a typical period on a woollen mule would be only fifteen to twenty minutes. In addition, soft twisted condenser yarns would neither snarl so readily nor, because of their greater resilience, nick so easily as typical fine cotton yarns.

Before long, however, woollen spinners began to demand more elaborate machines catering for their special needs. The machinery makers responded so enthusiastically that in a number of ways the later woollen mules became even more elaborate than their cotton counterparts. Very often woollen mules had the side rim arrangement in place of the back rim arrangement—a feature usually, but not invariably, found in cotton mules. The mule by William Whiteley & Sons of Huddersfield, illustrated on page 134 was typical of the late period machines. Most of the usual motions were present and some additional motions, including a two-or three-speed driving arrangement. These further elaborations were needed because condenser spinning is essentially a three-stage operation. First a length of roving, from one-quarter to two-thirds of the length of the draw, is fed quickly through the rollers while the carriage recedes at substantially the same speed, and the spindles rotate relatively slowly. The rollers are then stopped, or greatly retarded, and the speed of the spindles is increased in relation to the carriage speed during the remainder of the draw. This is a most critical part of the process in which, by maintaining a delicate balance between the rate of twist insertion and the rate of attenuation of the roving, a degree of yarn uniformity is achieved which far surpasses that attainable by conventional drafting. On completion of the draw there is a short period of twisting at the head, usually carried out at an even higher spindle speed. The backing-off and winding part of the cycle then takes place in the usual fashion.

The action of a woollen mule is extremely rapid. Although the draw is very much longer, usually in the range 72 to 84 in against the typical cotton draw of 63 or 64 in, the cycle time is very much shorter—shorter even than a coarse Oldham-type mule. This is, of course, a direct result of the very small amount of twist needed in woollen yarns: but it is, nevertheless, most impressive to see these great mules running at speeds in excess of five draws per minute when one is used to the more leisurely pace of fine mules.

Various means were employed to implement the complex drawing requirement, outlined above, at the highest possible speed. Among mules of the traditional type, those using typical nineteenth-century devices such as fast and loose pulleys and flat-belt drives, perhaps the best performance was achieved by machines equipped with a three-speed drive to the spindles and variable diameter scrolls for drawing out the carriage. With this arrangement the speed of the drawing out scroll shaft, which replaced the back shaft of the cotton mule, was uniform throughout the outward run: but the carriage speed was progressively reduced during the actual drawing period (ie after the stopping of the roving delivery rollers). Meanwhile the spindles were driven at the lowest speed during the period of roving delivery, accelerated to second speed for the period of drawing, and finally driven at maximum speed during twisting at the head.

What can be done using twentieth-century technology has been demonstrated by MaK (Maschinenbau) of Kiel, West Germany. This company in the 1950s introduced two completely new self-actors for woollen spinning. Both were hydraulically actuated. The first, known as the Wagenspinner, had the usual arrangement of a moving spindle carriage and stationary creel but the second, known as the Standspinner, had stationary spindles and a moving creel. The clean appearance of both the mule and, more particularly, the headstock of the Standspinner can be seen on page 152.

The productivity of these new machines is claimed to be more than twice that of conventional self-actors. Some of the gain is from the use of higher spindle speeds, some from the use of longer draws and a little from more expeditious backing-off and winding. A number have been installed in a Yorkshire mill and they are most impressive machines. All the spindles are gear driven separately so that there is no possibility of band slippage. Hydraulic variable speed units replace the fast and loose pulley arrangement of the conventional self-actor and virtually everything runs on ball bearings. Instead of changing gears and pulleys, alterations to the cycle are made by merely setting dials on the front of the headstock. Briefly one can say that these new automatic mules have the same relationship to the old self-actor as the modern electric or diesel railway locomotives have to the old steam locomotive.

Whether or not this new-look mule will be commercially successful remains to be seen, but the mere fact that it has been produced at all is ample proof of the particular suitability of the mule for the production of woollen yarns.

9

The Work of the Spinner

WHEN a group of Manchester mill owners commissioned Richard Roberts to design a self-acting mule, their principle objective was to break the power of the very militant operative spinners' unions. The manually controlled mule made such severe demands on the spinner that only adult males could operate it. Not only was the work extremely arduous but it also required a sensitive touch and continuous, close attention in a hot humid atmosphere. One man, assisted by two or three females or juveniles, was needed for each pair of mules: but his contribution was merely the mechanical actuation of the machines. It was naturally expected that with the development of a satisfactory self-acting mule no human actuation would be needed. The mules would then be tended by cheap female or juvenile labour and set and maintained by specialist mechanics.

That these expectations were never realised in Britain is a fact difficult to explain. At the close of the eighteenth century, spinning and weaving had a great deal in common. They were both completely dependent on the work of skilled male tradesmen. A number of ancillary tasks were performed by women and young people, but in both cases skilled adult men were needed for the arduous and exacting work of actuating the machines. The problems of power-loom weaving were solved some years before the self-acting mule became a practical proposition, and steam weaving was well established and rapidly increasing in popularity by about 1815. By 1833 roughly 100,000 power looms were in use in Britain, and although the number was increasing very quickly it was lamented that the machine makers of Lancashire, among them Richard Roberts' firm, Sharpe, Roberts & Co, could not make them sufficiently fast to meet the needs of the manufacturers.

The enthusiasm of the manufacturers for steam weaving was largely a result of the fact that, despite a deal of riotous opposition by hand-loom weavers, it had been found possible to use very cheap labour to tend the new machines. Baines recorded that, in 1833, a very good hand-loom weaver aged twenty-five to thirty (ie in his prime) could weave only two 24 yd pieces of shirting in a week yet a teenage boy, assisted by a twelve-year-old girl, could tend four steam looms and produce 18 to 20 similar pieces in a week. Recognising that this system of loom operation must ultimately prevail, Baines makes the plea:

> It is earnestly to be desired that the whole number (of hand loom weavers) should be thus transferred to other branches of industry, as they have no prospect from continuing to toil at the hand-loom, but increasing misery and degradation.

By this time it was clear that misery and degradation had already become the lot of the hand-loom weaver. At the beginning of the century a weaver earned about 25s (£1·25) a week, but by 1830 his wages had fallen to only 6s (30 p) against an average for all trades in Lancashire of 22s (£1·10). This caused great concern and was the subject of a number of commissions of enquiry: but so far as the manufacturers were concerned it was a fait accompli and the grip of the craft union had been broken for ever. It became, and remains, the practice to employ relatively cheap labour to tend power looms which are only tuned and serviced by tradesmen.

What had happened to the weavers was a dire warning to all spinners. During the period in which the new system had been introduced into weaving, harsh application of the combination laws had prevented the weavers effectively opposing the innovation. The spinners were under no such disadvantage when their turn came. The repeal of the combination laws in 1824 was quickly followed by the emergence of an extremely strong and closely knit operative-spinners' organisation determined at all costs to maintain the tradesman status of the operative spinners. In this they were completely successful and, throughout the whole period during which mules have been used to spin cotton, the system of staffing in Britain has been one which recognises the spinner as a tradesman selling the fruits of his labour.

In the early days of the self-actor this situation was entirely justified, for, as we have seen, it took almost fifty years to perfect such important accessories as the strapping and nosing motions. Later it would have been technically feasible for mules to be staffed like looms. Indeed this became normal practice in America, but in Britain the old order was maintained. Strong union opposition to change was an important factor: but there was also the considerable practical difficulty that every operative spinner was firmly of the opinion that no two mules could ever be made alike. As a consequence he proceeded to tune and adjust each of his own particular pair of mules with little respect for the intentions of the maker or the principles of engineering. Before very long, no two mules ever were alike.

This state of affairs was not peculiar to the spinning industry, it was widespread. It need not have been so, for the principles of interchangeable manufacture were being increasingly applied to the making of textile machinery, and much could have been done to standardise maintenance and setting procedures on the mule. In the event little was done. It continued to be necessary to have one fully qualified spinner to look after each pair of mules and, because of the many small peculiarities which the individual approach to tuning engendered, it was usually unwise to move a spinner about other than in exceptional circumstances. Thus each spinner became identified with a particular 'pair' which he regarded as his own and it was not unusual for him to continue to operate that same pair for twenty, thirty or even forty years.

The organisation of the typical spinning mill was extremely simple. Such subtleties as functional organisation with horizontal links were not even a remote possibility. The industry was wholeheartedly geared to the simplest possible line-and-staff form of organisation with crystal-clear demarcation of responsibility at every level.

At the head was the general manager (often a director or partner). So far as matters external to the mill were concerned, he would be assisted by a secretary and a salesman. For everything within the mill, the general manager worked through an inside manager who controlled all internal activities. Responsible to the inside manager were four men, the engineer, the carder, the spinning-room overlooker and the warehouseman. The engineer was responsible for providing power at the line shaft, but not an inch beyond. His staff attended to everything connected with power generation, right up to the lubrication and adjustment of the line-shaft bearings; but the driving belts by which power was taken from the line shafts were the responsibility of the department using the power.

The carder was responsible for all processes preparatory to spinning, from the opening of the bales of raw cotton to the delivery of roving bobbins into the spinning room. Normally all preparatory processes were carried out on the ground floor and the spinning mules were contained in the upper three or four floors. A powered hoist was used to take the roving bobbins up to the spinning room and this was operated by the bobbin carrier, a member of the carder's staff, whose task it was to deliver the bobbins to each pair of mules as required.

The spinning-room overlooker, often referred to as the mule gaffer, or simply 'the gaffer', was responsible for the actual spinning process. His responsibility started with receipt of the roving bobbins and ended with delivery of the cops of yarn at the entry to the hoist by which they were taken down to the cellar by a member of the warehouseman's staff.

The warehouseman was responsible for conditioning, ie ensuring that the yarn contained exactly the permitted quantity of water, and for the packing and despatch of all orders. Communication between the spinning room and the cellar was almost entirely dependent on small square labels of colourful paper, used to identify each skip of yarn delivered to the cellarman's hoist. Each label, coloured to identify the cotton quality, was boldly printed with the yarn count number and the words weft or twist. The spinner added, in indelible pencil, the number of the mule and the date of doffing. Later the warehouseman would be responsible for adding the net weight

Page 151: *One of the few remaining mule rooms in Lancashire. The author is in conversation with the minder*

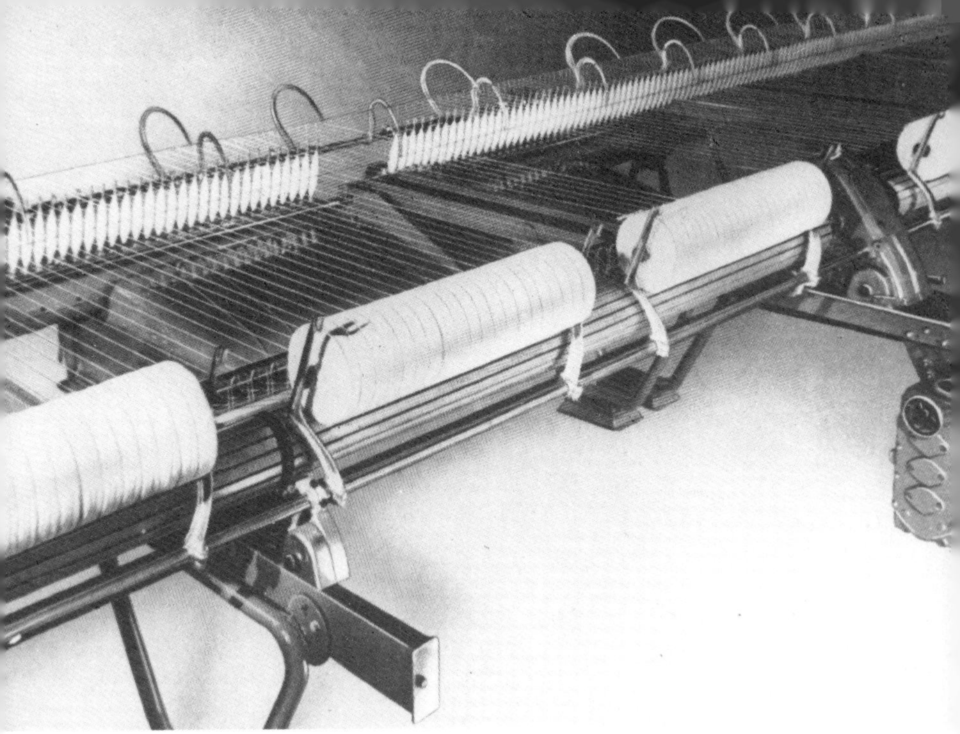

Page 152: (above) The MaK Standspinner, c 1956, (below) Rollers of a Bolton-style mule

in each skip. Nor was there any more communication between card room and spinning room, just a label with a printed hank number and a pencilled frame number. Each department of the mill ran as a self-contained, highly specialised entity responsible only to the inside manager.

The gaffer himself was normally the only channel of communication between the spinning-room staff and the rest of the mill and, in addition to his administrative function, he invariably took complete responsibility for all technical matters. Today no spinning mill is complete without a quality-control department equipped with a variety of highly scientific instruments and employing quite sophisticated quality control techniques: but in those days quality control was left entirely to the gaffer. At the worst his equipment was no more than a simple balance and a wrap reel, but quite often it would include a quadrant-type yarn-strength tester. With these and a ready-reckoner he checked the count of the yarn from each mule at regular intervals and ordered gear changes to be made whenever his wrappings indicated a departure from the required count. He was responsible too for the scheduling of work and issued precise instructions, usually on a pro forma, whenever changes in count or twist factor were needed.

An under-gaffer was employed to assist the gaffer and often he was a man who had been trained as a mule fitter at the works of one of the machinery makers. He would normally be responsible for the repair of major breakdowns and the reconditioning or modification of machines carried out from time to time. Both the gaffer and the under-gaffer were distinguished from all other spinning-room workers by the fact that they wore boots—everyone else worked barefoot. The gaffer himself invariably wore immaculate whites—white trousers and a jacket—but the under-gaffer more commonly wore a dark-blue overall suit. Each had his own 'cabin', usually a small room opening out of one of the spinning rooms. The gaffer's cabin, which was used as an office and, in today's phrase, a quality-control laboratory, was always unbelievably clean and tidy: every inch of the bare wooden floor was maintained to a dazzling white by frequent scrubbings with hot water, soft soap and sand. Although the under-gaffer's cabin could not be kept in the same pristine condition, being more an engineer's workshop than an office, it was generally kept spick and span.

Only the gaffer and the under-gaffer had duties of a general nature. The rest of the spinning-room workers were directly engaged in spinning; they were divided into many identical cells, each one consisting of three people and being solely concerned with the operation of one particular pair of mules. The structure of the cell was the same throughout the kingdom. The senior member, officially styled an operative spinner but usually referred to as the minder, exercised absolute authority over his two assistants. The pair of mules was regarded as his, and he was paid, each week, a sum of money directly and precisely related to the amount of yarn he had spun in the preceding week. Out of this he paid his two assistants their fixed standard wages. These wages were determined, by local agreement, in relation to the size and gauge of the mules, but they were not dependent on production: thus only the minder was subject to a financial incentive.

The younger of the two assistants was universally known as the little piecer. In Oldham the other was called a big piecer and in Bolton a side piecer. Generally this team of three did everything that was needed to keep their own particular pair of mules working at peak efficiency week in and week out. No outside help was called for except on an informal reciprocal basis with near neighbours.

Earlier chapters described in considerable detail the work done by the mule but so far little has been said about the equally important part which men and women played, and continue to play, in the spinning of yarn. Essentially the work is concerned with four basic textile tasks which are common to all systems of machine spinning and which are all likely to continue to be performed by human hands for many years to come: they are described below.

CREELING. This is the necessary periodic replenishment of the supply of roving from which the yarn is being spun. Usually the roving was supplied to mules from individual bobbins, each mounted with its axis vertical to turn freely on a pointed wooden skewer supported in a framework called the creel. The weight of roving on a full bobbin varied from 6 or 8 oz on mules for medium and fine yarns, to 1 lb or more on the coarsest mules. Naturally the length of time which each creel bobbin lasted was governed by a number of factors, the most important of which was the count being spun. On very coarse counts a bobbin would run no more than a couple of days, but on say 80's, two to three weeks was a more usual life. In order that one person could keep pace with the work it was the practice to arrange that the bobbins ran out sequentially in successive sections of the creel.

Creeling was done without interruption of the spinning process. When a section was about to start to run empty the creeler would take up his position behind the mule, having previously arranged a supply of full bobbins conveniently on the shelf which formed the top of the creel. As each bobbin in turn was about to run empty the creeler would pick it out of the creel and, in a single deft motion, unreel a foot or so of roving, breaking it at a convenient length, and slip the bobbin from its skewer into a skip. He would then pick a new bobbin from the creel top with the aid of the skewer and, as he inserted the skewer and bobbin into the creel with one hand, would join the end of the new roving to the fast disappearing tail of the old with the other hand. The action was done very quickly and usually so neatly that the joint would pass through without causing any trouble more than a barely perceptible local thickening of the yarn.

PIECING. Even the most highly developed spinning machines suffer to a greater or lesser extent from sporadic yarn breakage, and piecing, the repair of broken ends, is a never-ending task so long as spinning is in progress. For all spinning machines the frequency with which breakages occur depends on the running speed, the twist factor used and, most of all, on the quality of the roving. Unfortunately high quality roving costs money, but so too does piecing labour. In consequence, the breakage rate is often largely an economic compromise between these two factors. Conditions today are such that average breakage rates of the order of 1·2 to 1·5 per 100 spindle hours are achieved on modern high-speed ring frames: but in the heyday of the mule breakage rates were roughly ten times greater.[1] Thus on a pair of typical late period mules of 1,200 spindles each, about five or six ends would be breaking each minute. Clearly the work of repairing broken ends could never be neglected for more than a few minutes and was a most important staple task.

On ring frames and throstles, piecing is complicated by the need to thread the yarn through the traveller and guide-eye (on the former) and through the flyer-arm guides (on the latter). On the mule there was no such complication, as the yarn path from rollers to spindle tip was quite free. To repair an end broken during spinning was simplicity itself. The yarn end quite naturally coiled into a snarled, fuzzy bunch, or whorl, on the tip of the spindle while the roving end was picked up by the underclearer (or on Bolton mules the fluker rod). It was only necessary to grip the snarled, fuzzy bunch between finger and thumb of the right hand; draw off a length of unsnarled yarn and lay it round the index finger and between thumb and first finger of the left hand; break off the yarn close to the point where it was gripped by the left hand; and, finally, bring the yarn into contact with the roving by pressing the index finger against the fluted bottom roller and releasing the yarn end as contact was made.

This was, of course, a dynamic operation performed very quickly with the mule running at full speed. Only the last act of the sequence required any real measure of skill. The actual contact of finger and roller was made with a slight rolling motion and at the same instant the grip of first finger and thumb on the yarn end was relaxed sufficiently to allow twist to run through and unite yarn and roving. After a piecing had been made it was usually necessary to adjust the yarn coils on the spindle blade so that at the next backing-off the repaired end behaved exactly as did its neighbours. This was very quickly and easily done.

For the repair of an end broken during winding there was the additional task of finding the end. Sometimes this could be done

[1] A hundred years ago 1 lb of good American cotton cost about 20d (8½ p). A similar cotton can be bought today for less than 40d (16½ p) but wage rates have increased more than ten-fold. This has, of course, profoundly influenced the cost relationship of cotton to piecing.

without stopping the spindle but more usually it was necessary to stop the spindle, by gripping it with the finger of the left hand and drawing the end from the chase of the cop with the right hand to form a fuzzy bunch at the spindle tip. From this point onwards repair was exactly as for an end broken during spinning.

The actual piecing could only be done during the part of the spinning cycle in which the operative could reach to touch the rollers. As the carriage came out the operative, facing the rollers, had to move backwards with it. An average adult could reach far enough to effect a piecing for about half of the draw—usually a period of three or four seconds from the commencement of spinning. He could, of course, make such preparations as forming a convenient tip bunch at other times in the cycle. There were also such time-saving expedients as taking the process to the penultimate stage before backing-off, holding the spindle stopped during the run-in and touching the yarn to the rollers the instant spinning recommenced. When a number of ends were broken in close proximity a really expert piecer could get up as many as five in a single draw. More usually, however, with breakages occurring here and there at random, a lot of walking was involved (a 1,200-spindle 1¼ in gauge mule was over 130 ft long) and an average breakage rate for a pair of mules of five or six per minute was enough to keep two piecers pleasantly occupied. When, for short periods, spinning was bad or one piecer was engaged in other duties, this rate could be doubled.

DOFFING. This is the third task common to all systems of machine spinning: the removal of completed yarn packages from the spindles. On other systems the task is complicated by the fact that bobbins are needed, but on mules which formed a cop on the bare spindle it was extremely simple. First the mule was stopped on the inward run, with the faller at its lowest position and with the counterfaller hooked down to allow the ends to go slack. While the minder returned all the progressive motions, such as the copping rail, the quadrant nut and the nosing peg, to their initial positions, the piecers would go along the length of the carriage raising the cops an inch or so up the spindles. This operation, known as thrutching-up, was carried out very quickly—three, four or (with small cops and a large hand) five at a time.

When thrutching-up was completed the minder would run the mule in a little to wind a few turns of starting yarn on the spindle blade just below the raised cops. The piecer and the minder would then each dash along from right to left, facing the carriage, removing the cops three or four at a time with the right hand and piling them neatly on the left forearm and hand. At intervals the doffed cops would be deposited equally neatly in conveniently placed skips. The whole operation was carried out with disciplined haste so that in only a very few minutes all 1,200 spindles were bare and ready for the resumption of spinning. The yarn, having broken between the starting yarn and the old cop, and no bobbins being needed, the mule was restarted the instant the last cop was removed from its spindle and the operation of doffing was over.

In order to get very firm cop bottoms it was common to whip the first few layers of yarn. This was done after three or four draws had been completed. The mule would be stopped at the beginning of the inward run and then taken in slowly while intermittently depressing the winding faller to put a succession of part turns just below the cop bottom as binders. Firmness was also achieved by pasting. This too was done after completion of three or four draws. The mule would be run out at reduced speed while the piecers walked briskly along applying a starch paste to the layers of yarn on the rotating spindles by means of a patent paste applicator. Although a cheap and extremely effective way of firming the bottoms, pasting required nice judgment for the first layers of yarn to adhere to each other but not to the spindle blade. In later years it became increasingly common to use a short paper tube to support the cop bottom, and it was necessary to press these tubes onto the spindle before resuming spinning after doffing. As the use of paper tubes slightly complicated the doffing procedure and materially increased the time taken, a compensatory payment was made to minders when spinning on tubes.

CLEANING. This, the final task, has a number of common elements in the various systems of spinning but the details vary greatly. The rapid motion and high frequency of vibration of the yarn during spinning tends to release a lot of fly (short fibre) into the air. This fly tends to accumulate on the working elements of the spinning machine and sooner or later, is disturbed and becomes attached to the yarn. This is most undesirable as the resulting slubs are very objectionable in the finished cloth. To avoid this trouble all critical areas are regularly cleaned, either automatically or manually, at intervals suited to the situation.

On mules, the two most critical areas were the carriage top immediately behind the spindles and the region of the drafting rollers. Most mules had flannel-covered clearer rollers which ran in contact with the top drafting rollers to pick up and retain short fibres. They were very easily removed and cleaned as required. On Oldham-style mules flannel-covered underclearers, rollers about 1 in in diameter and 12 in or so long, ran in contact with the lower surface of the bottom front roller. These sticks or crows were held up by spring clips and served also to collect waste roving from broken ends. If an underclearer became overloaded with fly or roving there was always the risk that it would stop turning. If this happened and then an end broke the waste roving would be blown about, bring down many adjacent ends and create a lot of additional work for the piecer. The removal of fly and roving from the underclearers was therefore a routine task second only in importance to piecing.

The task of piking the sticks was made difficult by the fact that they were below the yarn sheet, and on weft mules the pitch of the spindles and hence the distance between the ends was only 1¼ in. It was, however, possible to slip the hand and wrist between adjacent ends and remove a stick without breaking an end. It was also possible to replace the clean stick in the same way. Normally a piecer would remove two sticks, one with each hand, at the beginning of a draw, strip them and slip them back beneath the yarn sheet during the next inward run, and finally click them crisply into place at the instant of let-in. As, during re-insertion, the sticks were turned through a right angle in the rapidly decreasing space between the spindles and the roller beam, there was a risk of the sticks or the piecer's hands, or both, being trapped between the faller wires at unlocking, and the whole operation was a most impressive feat of sleight-of-hand. The occasional virtuoso could embroider the performance by rapidly removing, stripping and re-inserting one additional stick during the first moments of the draw to achieve a total piking rate of three sticks per draw.

Cleaning the carriage top and the roller beam with the mule running was a more difficult matter. A scavenger cloth cleaned most of the carriage top automatically but it could not safely be set to clean the vital few inches immediately behind the spindles. This cleaning operation, known as wiping down, was done by the two piecers working simultaneously, each in his own half, in a ritual established and followed in the interests of speed and safety. The mule was stopped with the carriage in such a position that a piecer crouching beneath the yarn sheet could just reach the spindle rail with the cloth held in his left hand, and the roller beam with a brush held in his right hand. The piecer would then run along, bent double with his head down and his back just clear of the yarn sheet, keeping the cloth in contact with the spindle rail and the brush in contact with the roller beam. It was not an easy journey. Each slip was a hazard on which one might stub a bare toe, and carriage wheels and drawbands were additional hazards, but most important of all was the presence of the yarn sheet immediately above one's head. Even the briefest of contacts with the yarn would bring down scores of ends—and, of course, the minder's wrath, forcibly expressed.

The ritual of the operation was primarily concerned with the stopping and re-starting of the mules. Each piecer would wipe down his own half of the mule, and before the mule was stopped the two piecers would take up a position convenient for entering below the creel, ie from behind the mule, yet where they could clearly see, and be seen by, the minder standing in front of the headstock. The minder would then stop the mule on the outward run, and signal that it was safe to enter by raising both hands above his head. The two-hand signal gave assurance that the 'stang' by which the drive-belt position was controlled was securely latched and not merely held in the minder's hand. After wiping down, the ritual was concluded by the piecers proceeding to agreed positions of safety, in which they were visible to the minder and standing erect. Only then would the minder put his hand to the stang and restart the mule.

How many little piecers were accidentally crushed between carriage and backstops as a result of a stumble or a misunderstanding, before the need for a very rigid procedure was established, is not known. Certainly it was a hazardous situation in which a minder, unable to see positively that his piecer was clear, might see another boy moving behind the creel, wrongly assume that it was his boy and restart the mule with disastrous consequences. Early wiping-down rituals, evolved in different districts, varied in detail, but all had the same laudable object of eliminating the risk of a misunderstanding. Ultimately they led to the adoption of a uniform procedure which was codified and made mandatory by statute.

There was a clear division of responsibility for the running of each pair of mules. From the main access alley to the headstock of each mule of the pair was known as the minder's half. Beyond the headstock was the big piecer's half. Normally the minder was assisted in the routine task of piecing by the little piecer, but the big piecer was expected to keep his half up unaided. Menial tasks such as floor-sweeping and weft-carrying were done for both halves by the little piecer.

The minder himself was solely responsible for the maintenance of the headstock and the precise adjustment of its many motions. Most minders took this responsibility seriously. Few were content to tolerate the least falling-off in performance and many were ever striving to tune the more important motions to a pitch of performance beyond the dreams of the inventors. Almost all minders were convinced that even the most carefully set-up self-actor fell short of perfection, and few could resist the temptation to make small overriding adjustments to the strapping and nosing motions during the building of each set of cops. The importance of this part of the minder's work was small; it would certainly not be countenanced by modern management consultants using value-analysis techniques.

Maintenance of the various straps and bands, however, was of the greatest importance. The main driving strap from the line shaft to the countershaft gave little trouble. It was generously proportioned and, having a long horizontal run providing adequate catenary tension, its exact length was not particularly critical. The downstrap was another story. The near-vertical layout, dictated by space considerations, meant almost complete dependence on elastic strain in the strap for adequate driving tension. Most important of all, the very severe conditions obtaining as the strap was moved onto the fast pulley to accelerate spindles and carriage at the beginning of each draw caused relatively rapid wear and extension. Because his wage was dependent on the speed of his mules, every minder developed a high sensitivity to the performance of the downstrap. At the first sign of undue slippage he would collect his tools and spare laces together and as soon as was convenient, perhaps during the dinner hour, he would unlace the joint and relace it one or two holes tighter.

Perhaps the most sensitive band of all was the check (or front) scroll band. The function of this band was deceleration of the carriage during the latter part of each inward run. It was secured to the scroll by a special knot, passed round a pulley at the front of the headstock and secured to the carriage by one form or another of patent clamp. Although the main claim of the special knot was equalisation of tension in the strands of the rope it was almost always here that it failed. If the imminence of failure was heralded, by a heavier than usual let-in of the carriage, the minder would sprint to the headstock and hope to stop or check the mule before the next let-in. As the distance from the out end of the mule to the headstock of the long side was about 25 yd and the time available was of the order of ten seconds he had a sporting chance and usually made it. Excess band was always left outside the clamp, and it was only necessary to release the clamp and draw through another foot or so, cut off the frayed end and renew the knot, re-tighten the clamp and adjust the band tension. Only when all the spare had been used up was it necessary to fit a new band.

The front scroll band also required a little attention from time to time during the day. First thing in the morning with everything running cold, the engine speed would often be a little slow. This in itself would tend to give a rather sluggish let-in of the carriage, but the situation would be aggravated by the fact that the band would have shrunk a little as a result of the rising humidity during the night. During the next hour or so the band would stretch again and the engineer, anxious to get in his quota of engine revolutions for the day, would allow the speed slightly to exceed the norm. These two factors together would lead to a heavy let-in, with the carriage crashing noisily on the back stops. It was necessary, therefore, for the minder to think ahead, slackening the band before starting in the morning and progressively tightening it during the morning.

All the other bands and straps required some attention and, of course, renewal from time to time, but by far the most demanding was the rim band. This ran on double or triple-grooved pulleys and followed the rather intricate path shown in Fig 13. It was very heavily loaded as it ran at high speeds (up to 90 ft per sec), and handled both the power to accelerate the spindles at the beginning of each draw and the power to decelerate them for backing-off. The band, usually of $\frac{5}{8}$ to $\frac{3}{4}$ in diameter cotton rope, was made endless by a long running splice. The making of an almost undetectable long splice was an art in which minders took a great pride. It was, of course, necessary to thread the band correctly before making the splice, as nothing more irritating, or damaging to the dignity and authority of a minder, can be imagined than a perfect splice made with the band passing on the wrong side of, say, the faller shaft. In commenting on the difficulty often experienced in threading double and triple-grooved systems, Thornley attributes much of the trouble to the hurry and bustle attendant upon the fitting of a new rim band, and recommends to management the provision of a scale model showing the band's correct path.

Minders naturally spared neither trouble nor expense to keep their rim bands in the best possible condition. Some would hook-up the band at the end of the day to prevent overnight shrinkage; others, holding that this practice damaged the band, instead slackened the tensioning pulley so as to allow the band to shrink without strain. Many prepared and used unguents or dressings by which the life of the band might be prolonged. The recipes for these concoctions were passed on from father to son and often called for such unlikely ingredients as vinegar, glue, black treacle, beeswax and plumbago.

The drafting rollers too came in for their share of special attention from the minder. There would be an agreed weekly or monthly ration of re-covered top rollers and the minder would replace any worn ones as he thought fit. Before using any of the re-covered front rollers he would carefully pair them, as only rollers exactly equal in diameter would run satisfactorily together on a common mandrel. Pairing was done by comparison, using the cusp formed between the faller shafts as an engineer would use a V-block: a short straight edge placed in contact with the two rollers would reveal even the smallest difference in diameter.

New or old, all front rollers were treated to regular applications of dressing or varnish with the object of minimising roller laps. It was popularly believed that it was roughness of the rollers which caused fibres to adhere to the surface and ultimately to form laps, and the varnishes used were esteemed for the gloss they imparted to the leather. Today's view is that the generation of static charges is the root cause of lapping, and synthetic roller covers which are substantially free from this trouble are used on ring frames. Although the phenomenon may not have been fully understood the varnishes developed for this purpose were extremely effective; moreover, in ten or fifteen minutes all the front rollers of a 1,200 spindle mule could be treated without disturbing them.

Roller varnishes, like band dressings, were often prepared according to secret recipes, although no publication on spinning was complete which did not contain the particulars of at least one highly recommended preparation. The basic ingredients used had much in common with those listed for rim-band dressings, but the method of preparation was usually rather more involved and the ultimate consistency was commonly more fluid. In addition, a bright pigment such as lemon chrome or Brunswick Green was usually added—though its function may have been no more than decorative or even psychological.

10

Life in the Jennygate

ALTHOUGH Crompton's concept was based on an extension of the domestic system of spinning it was not long before powered mules were being operated on the factory system. The way of life which became established in the new factories was unique in British industry. Mule spinners began to form closely knit communities, proud of their craft and living a life apart, as do miners and fishermen today. Within these communities it was naturally expected that sons, in due course, would join Dad in the jennygate[1] and a father's greatest ambition was to see his sons settled, each a minder with a 'pair of his own'.

My own father was very proud to be a minder. His friends were minders too, and as a child, nothing seemed more natural than that I, in my turn, would one day go to the mill and be initiated into the mysteries of the craft. Unhappily, as a result of an accident in the jennygate my father lost his left leg and for many months hovered between life and death. When eventually he was able to get about a little on crutches it was clear that he would never be able to tend a pair of mules again. His only direct contact with the mill thereafter was to stump along to collect his compensation money of 25s (£1·25) a week, pending a full settlement.

My contact with the mill began on my tenth birthday. That was the age at which a boy was entitled to release from school at midday to take his father's dinner. Although my own father was

[1] Pronounced 'jinnygate', jenny being derived from 'engine'.

no longer in the mill, a near neighbour was in this respect regarded as standing in loco parentis to me. Each day at 11.45 I would dash home from school to collect my 'father's' dinner, or baggin. It was always piping hot, in a basin covered with a saucer, and tied up in a large, white-patterned red handkerchief. By midday I was one of a stream of small boys, all carrying similar basins tied in similar red handkerchiefs, converging on the mill entrance. There was a great clatter of clogs as we rushed through the big iron gates and up the steep stone steps to the spinning rooms, anxious to deliver our precious basins before a faltering of the engine note heralded the mass exodus of those who went home for their midday meal.

On entering the spinning room we stepped into a bewildering but fascinating new world. Men we knew, whom we had previously seen only in heavy dark clothes, were hardly recognisable barefoot and wearing only loose white corduroy trousers and thin white shirts. The exotic atmosphere too made a great impression on a young mind. It was hot, of course, but it was not a dry heat. It was hot and humid like some tropical jungle and the heat brought out a variety of scents, from the cotton itself, from the oil-soaked pinewood floor and from the mahogany carriages and creels. Above it all was the whir of spinning spindles, the shriek of tortured leather straps and the thump of carriages letting-in.

Somewhere in every spinning mill statutory notices were displayed prohibiting, in formal and ponderous phrases, all sorts of things including the entry of small boys into the mulegate itself. Naturally small boys did not waste time reading such notices but we were all aware of a much more real limitation of entry into the working space where the mule carriages ran. We were not allowed in while wearing clogs. The risk that a boy wearing clogs might easily slip on the oily floor was one consideration, but equally important was the chance that a broken clog iron might raise splinters on the floor which would be a hazard to barefoot piecers and minders. This was a limitation easily dealt with. Clogs were kicked off and for a few glorious minutes one could follow the carriage in and out and perhaps, if specially favoured, attempt to piece a broken end.

My fourteenth birthday found me ready for work. There may well have been careers advisers and juvenile employment bureaux offering formal channels of entry into industry at that date but we knew nothing about them in our neck of the woods. The only method of recruitment to the mill was by personal recommendation. As a disabled ex-minder my father had no real difficulty in persuading an old friend to be my sponsor. I was soon fitted out with clothing appropriate to my station and, on a cold winter's morning, was taken to the mill for my first day's work.

My father's friend was of some standing in the community being, in fact, the under-gaffer. In keeping with the dignity of his office he wore a bowler hat and carried a Gladstone bag containing his lunch. My soon-to-be-assumed status as a little piecer was much less demanding and I was content to wear a cloth cap and to carry my baggin, both lunch and dinner, tied up in the traditional red handkerchief.

It was about half-an-hour's walk to the mill and little was said as we strode through the darkness. Having only seen the mill in broad daylight before, I was very surprised, and not a little worried, to find everything in what at first appeared to be total darkness. After a few moments one realised that the darkness was not absolute. A few dim, but strategically placed, lights were just sufficient to enable the workers, who were now thronging the mill entrance, to find their way in and to remove their outdoor clothing.

We had been in the mill only a few minutes before the shadowy figures stopped moving through the gloom and the murmur of conversation ceased and gave way to an expectant hush. A few moments later a faint tremor ran through the building as, to a swelling chorus of creaks and groans, the line shaft started to turn. As the speed increased further the creaking and groaning died away and was replaced by a steadily growing rumble. At about the same time the main lights, which were powered by a generator coupled to the engine shaft, began to glow feebly.

Slowly, as the speed continued to increase, the lights grew brighter and soon I could see that I was in a very large spinning room, lofty and with walls and ceiling brightly lime-washed. Everyone had started work, the piecers were busy oiling the spindles and the minders were fussing about their headstocks. As the lights reached full brilliance minders everywhere were looking up at the line shaft and wondering when they dare risk a first draw. Stangs were pushed forward, the engine faltered a little before taking up the load and within a very few minutes every mule was running and the work of the day had really begun.

The mill was regarded as modern, having been built in 1906 and being then less than twenty-five years old. It was typical of the 1904 to 1910 boom mills in that it was of faced brick and, because of this, its outside appearance was very much smarter than that of the older mills of the district. Inside there was virtually no difference. It was a four-storey building with preparation on the ground floor and spinning on each of the upper three floors. The mill was an independent concern, not financially linked to any other textile company, and specialised in the production of a narrow range of yarns. Even for that time it was a large unit with a total of rather more than 110,000 spindles in three almost identical spinning rooms. Thirty weft mules, each of 1,392 spindles at 1⅛ in gauge, accounting for more than two-thirds of the total number, were in the bottom and middle spinning rooms. The top room housed the 1⅜ in gauge twist mules, each of 1,152 spindles, which made up the remainder. All had Oldham-style drafting but with only two ends to a boss—a compromise arrangement very suitable for spinning the medium fine counts of 60's to 100's in which the mill specialised.

The building, approximately 320 ft long by 150 ft wide, was designed expressly to house spinning mules. In each of the three spinning rooms thirty mules were arranged, as was usual, across the room as fifteen parallel, facing pairs with off-set headstocks, in the fashion introduced by McConnell and Kennedy in the 1790s (Chapter 3). The main access to the mulegates was from the minder's half, where there was a 3 ft alleyway between the frame ends and the wall. On the big piecer's half the gap between the frame ends and the wall was only 9 in. It was not difficult to step crab-wise through this gap to get from mulegate to creel alley and back, but it was too narrow for one to consider making longer journeys along that side of the room—except in emergency. Fixed iron escape ladders were provided on that side of the mill, and management probably considered that in the event of a serious fire the workers would be grateful for even a 9 in wide escape route.

The determination of management to get the maximum possible number of spindles into the space available was shown in the fact that the walls of the uppermost spinning room, not having to support any great weight, were thinner by two brick widths than the walls below them, though the outside faces of the walls were kept in the same vertical plane. Thus the top spinning room was 18 in wider than the rooms below and the mules in it could be longer by fifteen spindles.

The spinning rooms were lofty and well lit. In each, a line shaft ran the whole length of the room above the big-piecer's half. As the shaft was driven from one end only, and power was taken off at intervals along its 320 ft length, it was not necessary for it to be of uniform diameter: both expense and weight were saved by having it tapered, in steps, from about 8 in diameter at the driven end to about 4 in at the free end. The line shafts were all rope-driven, those in the spinning rooms running at a nominal 350 rpm. The rope race was built on the end of the mill and, as was usual in Lancashire, the multiple-rope system was used, each spinning room being driven through eight 2 in ropes running at the statutory limit for iron pulleys of 6,600 ft per minute.

The main engine itself was untypical. Most mills built about the turn of the century had twin tandem horizontal engines. They were double-acting onto two cranks fixed at right angles to each other on opposite sides of the flywheel. In each engine the high, medium and low pressure cylinders were co-axial and in tandem with a common piston rod running through all three cylinders to a single crosshead. This arrangement gave a very stiff crankshaft and easy access to all working parts. The fact that it took up rather a lot of room was unimportant for cotton-mill use. Our engine was very different: a four-cylinder, triple-expansion, vertical marine engine originally intended for a large passenger liner and developing 1,800 ihp. It was the wonder of the district that so compact an engine could drive so large a mill.

The spinning-room floors were laid with pinewood planking and the main alley was, in addition, overlaid with maple to withstand the relatively heavy traffic of shod feet. A simple railway, consisting of one flat and one edge rail, was also laid down the alley and on this ran a low, flat-topped bogie. The bobbin-carrier's hoist was at the end of the room in line with the alley and the bogie was primarily for his use when distributing the heavy skips of roving bobbins. Other users of the alley had to step into a convenient mulegate or creel alley to allow the bobbin carrier and his load to pass.

The amenities of the mill were minimal. There was no running water and no sanitary conveniences in the main block. An incredibly crude kitchen in which tea could be brewed and dinners warmed (there was, of course, no canteen) was provided at ground level; the equipment consisted of a large slop-stone with a single tap of cold drinking water, a steam-heated geyser which dispensed water hot enough for tea-brewing, and a large steam-heated oven. This served the whole staff, roughly 400 men and women.

The term 'sanitary convenience' could only be regarded as a euphemism at the mill. Two walled yards, open to the sky, which could be entered only from the short passageway connecting the lodge and the mill proper, each housed a block of six privies. The term convenience was particularly inappropriate for workers employed at the far corner of the top spinning room, who had a walk of 150 yd to the spinning-room door, a descent of six flights of stone steps and a short walk along a stone-flagged passage to reach the yard. After working in the heat of the spinning room on a fine summer's day it was perhaps pleasant to spend a few minutes in the coolness of the yard, passing the time of day with workmates while waiting one's turn in the queue, but on a bitter winter's day it held no attractions.

No taps or washing facilities were available in the sanitary compounds, or indeed anywhere else in the mill. The more fastidious dealt with the situation by using the fire buckets kept by each pair of mules for their ablutions. Each pair of mules had two two-gallon buckets and it was one of the little piecer's jobs to renew the water in these buckets from the one tap in the kitchen down at ground level.

I came to enjoy my days in the jennygate; although not easy the life was satisfying. It took a week or so to get used to working barefoot, to learn not to stub one's toes against the many iron projections from the floor but one soon learnt to be careful, and eventually the soles of one's feet became distinctly horny and almost spale-proof. But not quite; spales were always an occupational hazard and every minder carried a pair of tweezers (known as spale-nippers) in his pocket.

After a short period as a spare piecer, standing in for regulars temporarily absent, I soon became the regular little piecer on a pair of twist mules in the top room. From there the next step was promotion to the weft mules where, on account of the greater number of spindles to be tended, the wages were higher.

A piecer's working day started the instant the line shaft began to turn. At that instant we had to be ready, with full oil cans in our hands, to start oiling the bearings of the spindles. On hearing the first faint creak from the leather driving straps we would begin, the little piecer in the minder's half and the big piecer in his own half. The task was simple enough as the spindle bolsters were grooved to receive the oil, but one had to be careful to ensure that just the right amount of oil reached each bearing—not too little, or the spindle would run hot and make a soft yarn, not too much, or the excess would be thrown out and stain the cop bottoms. After a little practice one could start in the dark and oil all the 1,392 spindles of the half in about three minutes and have comfortable time to refill the oil can and dry one's hands before the engine was turning fast enough for spinning to begin.

For the first hour or so in the morning, and particularly after a cold night, keeping one's half up could be quite a hectic business. In addition to a much higher than normal end breakage rate there was always trouble with strings requiring replacement. The strings were the thin bands which drove individual spindles. They were by no means everlasting. Sometimes they would break and be thrown off, at other times they would run slack and make soft yarn: but every day three or four would require to be replaced in each half. The name of the genius who evolved the method of replacing the band without stopping the mule is not recorded, but he was certainly a man of courage. After lowering the access door at the front of the carriage, one crooked a finger over the part of the adjacent band which was running onto the spindle wharfe and pressed it downwards quickly and firmly. When done correctly this had the effect of guiding the band out of the wharfe and onto the bare spindle where, relieved of tension, it idled round in a leisurely fashion. Lack of firmness resulted in the finger being trapped and perhaps cut to the bone by the band, which was running at a speed of 50 or 60 ft per second.

Having slipped the adjacent band from its wharfe it was momentarily held and a new band tied to it with a slip knot. The other end of the new band was retained while the slip knot was allowed to go round the tin roller with the adjacent band. As the knot reappeared at the front of the carriage the tail was gripped to release the knot—and there was a new band safely threaded round the still running tin roller. It was then the work of a moment to knot the new band, slip it into place and cut off the loose ends. The adjacent band was returned to its wharfe by a dextrous flick of the finger, the two ends pieced up and the job was done. The task was not really difficult but boys who, lacking the confidence required when unslipping the running band, burnt or badly cut a finger at the first attempt were slow to master the technique, which was not made easier by the fact that it had to be done while following the carriage in and out.

As the temperature rose and the mules began to run more lightly the breakage rate would fall to a level such that a competent piecer could, with a bit of luck, 'keep all round up'. This was the signal for the little piecer to go down to the kitchen with three large jugs and brew the morning tea. Then odd jobs were tackled. Perhaps some routine cleaning would be done or roving bobbins would be laid onto the creel top ready for creeling.

Doffing was not so frequent a chore as in coarser mills. For month after month we spun 84's weft with a doffing cycle of nearly five hours and, this being a little longer than a half day, we normally had two doffings each day on each mule. Rather like the tides, the doffing came a little later each day until, roughly once a week, a day would come in which only one doffing was required; the first doffing the following day would then be a very early one. For the little piecer who had the job of carrying the heavy skips of weft on his shoulders to the cellarman's hoist, to have only one doffing made a red-letter day.

As doffing time approached we would make everything ready, ensuring that all ends were up on both mules, that no creel bobbins were likely to run out and that all the sticks were clean on the mule which would remain running. Two or three draws before actually stopping the mule the minder would signal readiness by striking the cast iron quadrant pinion cover of the headstock three times with a large spanner. Rather like the ritual sailing cries of 'ready about' and 'lee ho', made when putting a ship about, the clear ringing signal was always made before doffing, even though everyone concerned could be seen to be ready and waiting. Neighbours always helped at doffing time and it was done very quickly. As soon as the mule was running steadily again with all ends up (quite a few breaks were expected in the first few draws after doffing) the minder would tidy up the three or four skips of weft to show that he took a proper pride in his work, label each skip of the set and signal the little piecer to carry them to the hoist. Being a big strong lad this last task was no trouble to me but for many of those who were small for their years it was a trial.

They had the advantage over me when it came to wiping-down. This we did twice a day in the late morning and late afternoon. The time was chosen not because it was a job more easily done on an empty stomach, although this made quite a difference, but because a minder always liked to leave his mules clean and tidy at midday or evening. For the first few months this job was the bane of my life. Fortunately I had a philosophic minder quite content to lose a little on the swings in return for substantial gains on the roundabouts. With my generous build I could do many things the smaller boys could not do. As I could lay roving bobbins on the creel top with ease, needed no help in carrying the weft and, having long arms and hands like shovels, could doff as fast as any grown man, that I could not run quite so fast as the other boys when bent double under the ends was not too serious a matter.

As a growing lad with a hearty appetite dinner time was the highlight of the working day. Both my parents regarded the maintenance of one's body as almost a sacred duty; those who spent money on their backs at the expense of their bellies were roundly condemned as being unworthy of the bodies the Lord had given them. My mother was anxious that I should not outgrow my strength, and sent me off every morning with a sustaining main course in my basin, a meat and potato pie, a beef pudding or, best of all, a bacon hot-pot. Dinners were put into the steam oven at mid-morning and a few minutes before 12.15, when the engine would stop, the little piecer would be sent to bring them up and to brew tea for the minder, the big piecer and himself.

The engineer would blink the lights about thirty seconds before closing the regulator of the engine. Most minders would hang onto their stangs to get every possible draw in before stopping but long before the last slow creak of the line shaft coming to rest we were into our dinners. There was no room set aside for eating and we generally ate in the mulegates. Small groups of little and big piecers tended to form 'dining clubs', eating together regularly in the same mulegate. Most minders, being not so gregarious, dined in solitary state sitting on an upturned skip by the headstock. We, having less dignity, always sat on the floor with our backs to the mule carriage, having first placed pieces of cloth or old newspaper on the carriage and the floor to prevent our shirts and white trousers becoming oil-stained. Looking back, there are few meals taken in the best hotels which I have enjoyed quite so much as the bacon hot-pots I used to eat from a basin resting on the floor between my outstretched legs.

On very hot days in the summer we would forsake the mulegate and eat our dinners on one of the fire escapes. The escapes were over on the big piecer's half and that side of the mill faced south. Access was easily gained from a window. The escapes were all metal and at each floor level there was an iron chequerplate landing with guard rails. It was very pleasant to sit in the sun, 60 ft above the sparkling water of the mill lodge, and look across the open fields towards the smoky haze of distant Manchester. Often we would laze away the whole of the dinner hour just sitting up there above the world.

More usually, however, the weather did not tempt us out of doors and the time between finishing our meal and the line shaft starting to turn again was spent playing push-washer football. One slip of the mulegate was marked out for the game with goal posts at each end formed from inverted U's of faller wire. The 'players' were two large washers and the 'ball' a smaller washer. It was a game for two persons who played kneeling. The player washers were moved by striking them smartly with the blade of a pocket knife. The object, of course, was to get the ball washer through your opponent's goal. These games were keenly contested and we never seemed to tire of the pastime.

The afternoon passed very much as the morning except that it was fifteen minutes shorter and usually a great deal hotter. This would be particularly noticeable in the big piecer's half with its south-facing windows. In sunny weather when, for one reason or another, I was required to look after the big piecer's half I would fancy myself on the deck of a ship in the tropics. With the temperature around 100°F and bright sunshine streaming in through the large windows, oil used to bubble from the pinewood floor and the metal parts in the sun were hot to feet and hands. I used to look forward to the day when I too should become a big piecer and have a 'half' of my own.

(Local agreements were made as to the temperature range to be maintained. In the Oldham List 95°F was declared 'reasonable', but the agreement was vague, saying: 'the means of heating shall be turned off when the temperature reaches 95° and this agreement shall not be deemed to have been broken if under exceptional climatic conditions the temperature should rise above the figure named'. In my experience it was often 105°. Equal laxity prevailed in regard to the requirement relating to humidity. It was laid down that wet-and-dry bulb thermometers should be provided, but in both Oldham and Bolton Lists it was specially noted: 'No readings of the thermometers are required to be taken'.)

Not all days passed smoothly. From time to time we would all be at panic stations. Even the failure of one of the less-important bands would get the minder running around like a scalded cat, determined not to have the mule stopped an instant longer than was necessary. On these occasions the big piecer would keep the other mule running while I would act as labourer to the minder—passing tools and holding whatever happened to need holding. An unexpected failure of the twist (rim) band was a disaster of the first magnitude. With everything carefully prepared it was not an easy job. Done hurriedly without proper preparations it could be heart-breakingly difficult to the minder concerned and it was, therefore, prudent to keep a keen eye on the band and change it at a convenient time rather than wait for it to fly off unexpectedly.

The first step in preparation was the marking and cutting of a new band. In each room the required band length was marked out on the floor from a particular frame end. One end of the coil of banding was tied to that frame end, and the band was laid along the floor to beyond the mark. The minder would then persuade three or four of his friends to come along and help him to stretch the band: a piece of rove would be tied to it as a marker and the men would heave away like a tug-o-war team. The mule would then be stopped and the old twist band cut off. The more timorous minders would draw the new band into place by means of the old one, but usually there would be a more confident friend on hand ready to show just how easily a twist band could be put in place by a real expert. Once satisfied that the band was correctly threaded the minder would set about the job of making a perfect splice. This was usually done with the rope ends well wetted and the piecing when finished was about 12 in long, almost exactly equal in diameter to the rest of the band over the whole of its length.

The band was always pieced too short to go on the pulleys immediately, even with the adjustable tension pulley screwed in as far as it would go. It was then necessary to stretch the band and settle it into the grooves by running the mule. This seemed a somewhat hazardous business but I never heard of anyone being seriously hurt by it. The band was put into all grooves except the outermost one of the guide pulley at the front of the headstock. The remaining bight of the band was then passed round a small pulley which was freely mounted on an iron strap to which a rope tail 4 or 5 yd long was attached. The other mule would then be stopped; three or four men would take hold of the rope tail and, sitting on the floor in the gate of the other mule with feet braced against any convenient projection, pull to tension the new twist band. The minder would then push the stang cautiously forward to start the rim shaft turning. As the twist band gathered speed it began to stretch like elastic and the men on the floor hauled away at the rope tail to maintain the tension. This would be continued for two or three draws until the new band was long enough to be sprung onto the last groove. This achieved, the job was regarded as completed, hands were wiped free of oil, brows wiped free of sweat and the minders returned to their own pairs and a swig of cold tea.

Perhaps the most exasperating experience of all was to see a sawney caused by a moment's carelessness during doffing. With cops on the spindles a sawney was bad enough, but with the spindles bare and your wage stopped it was enough to make a minder weep. A piecer would be sent round to ask for assistance from all those the minder could call friends; they would come in person or send a piecer to help. Meanwhile, the minder would disengage the twist wheel so that the spindles could be run without driving either the rollers or the carriage. By the time the spindles were turning, most of the helpers were ready to start winding two or three layers of yarn at the base of the spindles. This was done very quickly, holding a cop in the left hand and guiding the yarn onto the running spindles with the fingers of the right hand. When sufficient yarn had been wound onto a spindle the right hand was lifted sharply and the yarn broken to leave a fuzzy bunch at the spindle tip.

In a surprisingly short time each of the 1,392 spindles had its starting layer and tip bunch of yarn. The spindles were then stopped and while the minder re-engaged the twist wheel his friends would start twisting-up the ends. Each underclearer was stripped or, if clean, turned to break the soft roving, leaving about 1 in protruding from the rollers. When piecing on a running mule the rotation of the spindles provided the twist needed, but with the mule stopped it was necessary to twist the yarn between finger and thumb until the end picked up the roving. When all had been twisted up the mule would be started gently, run out about a foot, and stopped. Usually about 90 per cent of the piecings would have taken, leaving between 100 and 200 ends down. These would be twisted up for a second time, with everything stopped, before letting the mule run normally. More than the usual number of ends would come down during the next few draws but the helpers would stay a few minutes until the situation was fully under control before going back to their own work.

But sawneys did not occur every day and a well-spliced twist band would run for a year or more. Generally life in the mulegate followed a smooth, well-ordered course. Every man and boy knew his place and knew exactly what was expected of him. There was a tacit assumption that it was a mere oversight that the hierarchy of mule spinning had not been set down in the first Book of Moses.

Just how long this pattern had existed it is difficult to say. There had been no changes between my grandfather's young days (c 1860) and my own except that mules had become longer and hours had become shorter. The Bolton List, defining the duties and scales of payment of minders and piecers, adopted in 1858, continued to be used into the 1940s. There were, of course, revisions of hours of work and rates of pay from time to time, but the structure remained unchanged. A similar list was used in Oldham over the same period. Both lists went into a great deal of detail about speeds, counts, twist factors and numbers of spindles. There were scales for extra tasks and for all manner of minor variants in machine construction.

At the beginning of the period the standard week was one of sixty hours; 6 am to 6 pm with $1\frac{1}{2}$ hours for meals from Monday to Friday and 6 am to 2 pm with a half-hour meal break on Saturday. In the 1870s, it was reduced to fifty-nine hours by ceasing work on Saturday at 1 pm. At about the same time the minimum age for full-time employment was fixed at thirteen years. The length of the working day remained unchanged throughout the working life of my grandfather and father. The number of hours worked per week was reduced to fifty-six and one-half by increasing the time allowed for meals, but up to July 1919 the engine started at 6 am and stopped at 6 pm. Then this was drastically curtailed, running from 7.45 am to 5.30 pm with only a one-hour break for midday dinner; this reduced the hours worked to forty-eight.

An account of life in the jennygate would not be complete without reference to spinner's cancer. From about 1900 onwards a high incidence of scrotal cancer was noted among mule spinners: the cancers were frequently fatal and usually afflicted spinners who had worked on mules for twenty or more years. The cause has not been precisely identified but it is believed to have been connected with the fact that from about 1880 onwards mineral oil began to be blended with the animal and vegetable oils used to lubricate the spindles. The spindles when running threw off a faint mist or spray of oil which contaminated the spinner's clothing in the region of the crotch, and both close contact and friction between clothing and body occurred each time the spinner leaned across the faller shafts to piece up a broken end.

The problem was given a great deal of attention in the 1920s and specially refined oils were introduced. These were not entirely successful and work was continued after the war. A specification for technical white mineral oils, believed to be completely non-carcinogenic, was established and it became a statutory requirement that mule spindles should be lubricated with either the approved white oil or animal or vegetable oil. All blends of mineral and other oils were prohibited. Whether or not this provision would have brought an end to spinner's cancer we shall never know.

An interesting feature of the disease is that its incidence was almost entirely confined to cotton-mule spinners. It did not afflict woollen or cotton condenser spinners. The explanation may lie in some critical threshold of tolerance. Cotton mules had more spindles at a closer pitch, the spindles ran a little faster and a little hotter and more frequent oiling was necessary. These factors combined to ensure that a greater quantity of more finely broken up oil was thrown onto the clothing of cotton spinners than onto the clothing of other spinners.

11

Decline and Fall

FROM the instant of Crompton's disclosure of its operating principles the spinning mule was extremely successful. It was particularly successful in its ability to spin a better yarn from a given cotton than could be spun by any other means. As no cheap home-grown cotton was available in Britain this was an important asset. Despite the mule's considerable disadvantage of being a very complex machine requiring highly skilled male labour for its operation, it rapidly became the almost universal spinning machine in Great Britain.

Although mules were widely used throughout the world there were some countries in which they never came to dominate the spinning industry. In America, where good cotton was relatively cheap and where the demand for men to maintain and operate complex mechanisms greatly exceeded supply, attention was directed to development of the simpler, more rugged throstle frame. Many patent high-speed throstles were introduced in the first quarter of the eighteenth century; all were true throstles and met with only limited success. It seemed that although faster-running throstles could be made, the higher capital and power costs involved were not really justified and generally the simple, common throstle won the day. This remained true until, in 1828, Charles Danforth of New Jersey and John Thorp of Rhode Island took out separate patents for a new continuous-spinning device.

Although the new machine was, at first, known as the Danforth

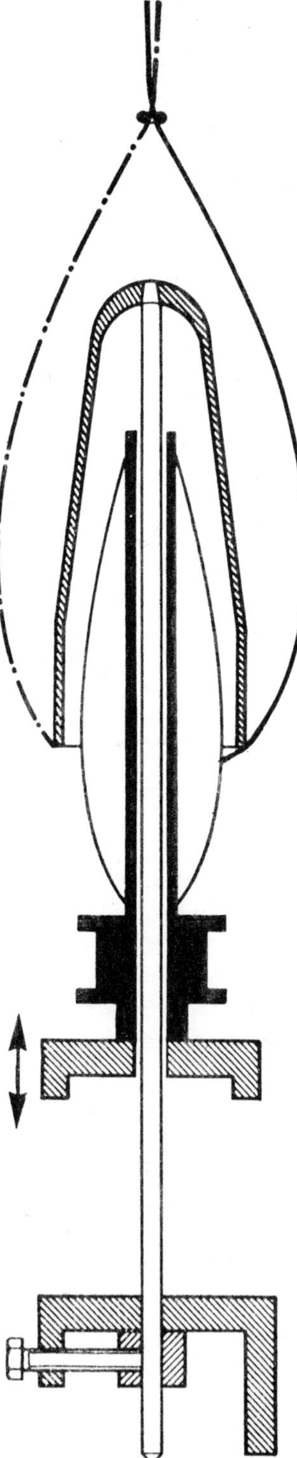

Fig 30. The Danforth Throstle (or cap frame). The yarn is guided by the lower edge of the stationary cap. A difficulty with this arrangement is that the cap must be removed before doffing the completed cop

throstle and had a superficial resemblance to the common throstle, it was misnamed, for it had no flyer. Danforth's machine, shown in Fig 30, had an upright dead spindle supporting a concentric hollow cone or cylinder called the cap or cape. The bobbin, carried by a sleeve running freely on the spindle and driven by a tape or band, was rotated at high speed within the cap. The path of the yarn from the drafting rollers was through a guide eye a little above and on the axis of the cap, down the outside of the cap, passing round its lower edge, or skirt, onto the bobbin. Danforth had found that when the bobbin was rotated at a high speed the yarn formed a stable loop describing a 'balloon' around the cap. Air drag on this rotating balloon, plus a little friction as the yarn was pulled around the skirt of the cap, was sufficient to wind the yarn firmly onto the bobbin. In order to distribute the yarn uniformly the bobbin and sleeve were moved slowly up and down within the cap. A combination of reciprocating and progressed movement was sometimes used to make a package rather like a mule cop and suitable for over-end unwinding.

This was a novel and ingenious machine and it was rapidly developed in America to operate reliably at 6,000 to 8,000 rpm. When introduced to Britain in 1829, however, it met with a cool reception. The reasons put forward by practical men for its rejection by cotton spinners in Britain are unconvincing, particularly as it soon became, and is still, widely used in the British worsted industry. It seems more probable that economic differences and the earlier introduction in Britain of Roberts' self-actor account for this parting of the ways. From this time onwards the Americans concentrated on the development of methods of continuous spinning for all fibres while the British proceeded to refine the mule further.

The ring spinning frame evolved slowly from the Danforth Throstle. Having appreciated that a stable, air-tensioned yarn balloon could be formed at high spinning speeds merely by the provision of a guiding element able to constrain the yarn to pass through a point whose locus was a circle, concentric with the spindle and in the plane in which winding onto the package was to take place, the search was on for the most convenient way of providing this guiding element. A difficulty with Danforth's solution was the need to remove the cap in order to doff the completed package: not a very serious difficulty, for doffing was even more of a problem with the true throstle frame.

Thorp's solution, patented in 1828—the same year as the Danforth and Thorp cap-frame patents—was a ring frame, but it was a ring frame without a traveller. The ring was a sandwich of two rings arranged to hold a round-section hoop loosely within a groove formed between the two component rings, as shown in Fig 31. The hoop performed exactly the same function as did the edge of the skirt of the Danforth cap. The yarn was able to pass freely between the hoop and the ring. This device, although perhaps rather difficult to thread, made doffing as simple as on the mule, and also permitted the use of a live spindle to support and rotate the package.

How well Thorp's ring frame worked is a matter for conjecture for, in the following year, Messrs Addison & Stevens patented the traveller, and spinning by ring and traveller developed very rapidly in the United States. The now common arrangement is shown in Fig 32.

The concept of a traveller, free to be drawn by the yarn around a suitably flanged ring, as a device to constrain the yarn path is elementary. That it should prove to be an eminently practicable way of spinning is most surprising. Travellers have been, and continue to be, made in a bewildering variety of shapes and materials but all have a great deal in common. Each is a small yarn guide, most commonly made from metal wire (although for some purposes moulded plastics are preferred), which is clipped onto the flange of a metal ring so formed as to permit the traveller to be drawn round freely by the yarn. At all spinning speeds the centrifugal forces generated by the movement of the traveller are very much greater than the centripetal forces which are applied by the yarn, and in consequence the traveller is pressed firmly against the inner constraining surface of the ring.

The durability of travellers in service is remarkable. Even with the materials available in the early nineteenth century, travellers had a life of six or eight weeks when running at 6,000 rpm around

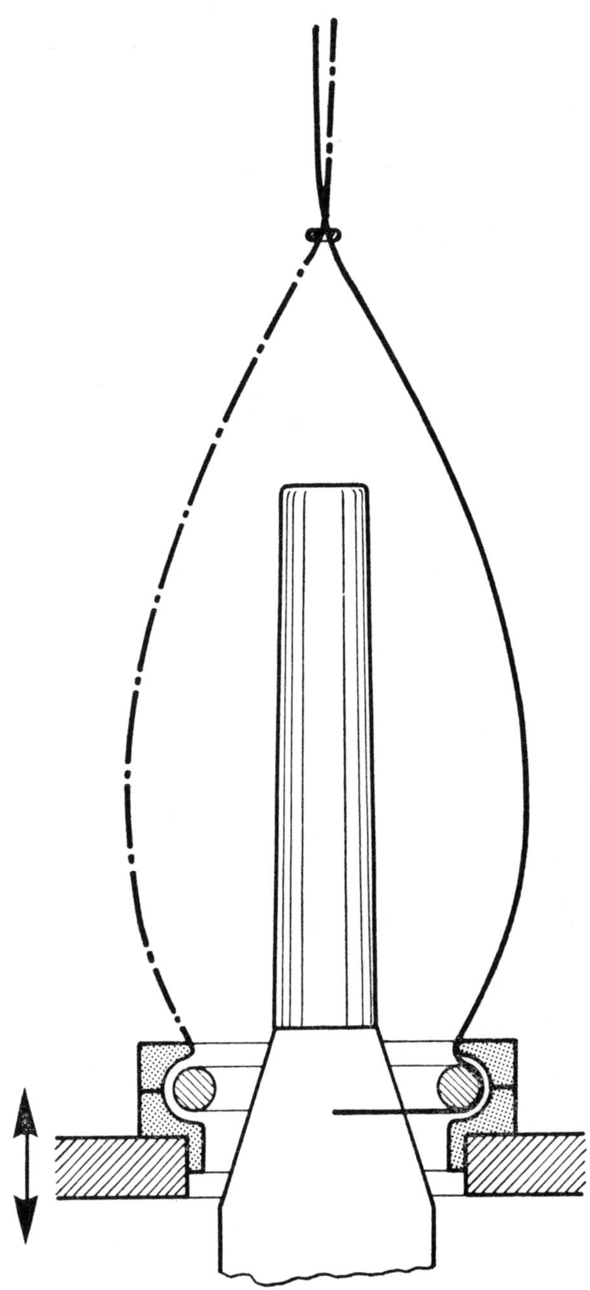

Fig 31. Thorp's Original Ring Spinner. This is not what is now termed ring spinning. Thorp's ring was floating and guided the yarn in exactly the same way as did the lower edge of Danforth's cap

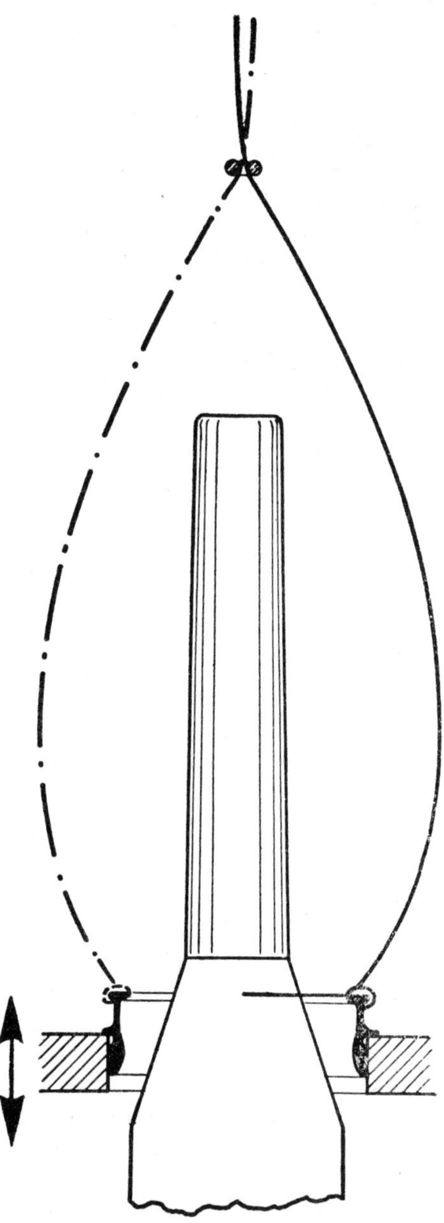

Fig 32. The Ring and Traveller Spinner. This is the system now known as ring spinning. The yarn is guided by a tiny 'C' shaped wire clip (the traveller) which is captive on, but slides freely round, the stationary ring.

a $1\frac{5}{8}$ in diameter ring. This corresponds to a total sliding distance of about 12,000 miles in an equivalent gravitational field of more than 800g. Modern travellers run at higher speeds and are a little more durable. Running at 12,000 rpm on a 2 in diameter ring, a sliding speed of rather more than 70 miles an hour, a steel spinning traveller typically has a life of 250 hours—a total sliding distance of 17,500 miles in a gravitational field of 4,000g.

In the United States the ring frame very quickly began to displace all other spinning machines. Long before the end of the century it was accepted as the universal machine capable of spinning yarns for all end uses in all fibre groups. In Britain, however, acceptance was slow indeed, and it was almost forty years before the first commercial ring-spinning unit was set up. By this time the self-acting mule had become very highly developed and was so versatile that it was, for many years, able to meet the challenge of the invader in all fields.

Despite the steadily growing popularity of the ring frame in other countries, most British spinners continued to prefer the mule until well into the present century. Their confidence that the future was with the mule was shown in the massive investment which, between 1905 and 1914, increased the number of cotton-spinning spindles by 15,000,000 to a total of almost 60,000,000. Of these, more than 80 per cent were mule spindles.

A justification for this investment was the fact that the weaving industry in Britain, which during the same period increased its complement of looms from 650,000 to 800,000, was almost completely dependent on Lancashire looms, for the shuttles of which the mule cop was ideal. In America, however, automatic looms were already finding rapid acceptance. For the shuttles of these looms special pirns, which could not conveniently be wound directly on either ring frames or mules, were preferred. For a time various expedients were employed to permit the direct use of mule cops, but generally the inconvenience was accepted and pirns were made directly on both mules and ring frames. Eventually, however, it became apparent that the most economic course was for the pirns to be wound as a separate operation after spinning. This led to the development of automatic machinery for rewinding all spun yarn, first onto cones or cheeses as a convenient intermediate package, and finally onto pirns for weft or onto beams for warp.

Once the practice of rewinding onto large intermediate packages was established, it began to be appreciated that this made it possible to monitor the yarn and remove such faults as slubs and clumsy piecings, which would otherwise cause trouble during weaving or be objectionable in the cloth. Almost fault-free weft made weaving a much easier task and, partly in order to attract labour, many firms began to use rewound weft even for Lancashire looms. When there was a shortage of weavers in Lancashire during the post-war textile boom of 1946 to 1951, it was common to see 'all re-wound weft' listed along with 'excellent canteen and day nursery' among the attractions of establishments anxious to recruit.

The coming of automatic yarn monitors, and later automatic electronic yarn clearers, so greatly increased weaving productivity and cloth quality that it soon became usual to rewind all spun yarn, whether for warp or weft. With this revolution in practice came a demand for larger and larger spun-yarn packages. When weft yarn had to be spun on packages small enough in diameter to fit directly into the loom shuttle, the ring frame was at a disadvantage to the mule. The situation was now changed in that the demand for larger packages was more easily met on the ring frame (where the package rotates steadily at a constant speed) than on the mule with its complex cycle of acceleration, deceleration and reversal repeated several times a minute. Technical difficulties were encountered at first, but before long the only real limitation on package size was the techno-economic consideration of the relationship between the cost of the additional power needed to drive a larger package and the saving in handling costs which resulted from the need to doff, creel and transport fewer packages. Typical ring-frame packages came to contain from five to six times as much yarn as did mule cops of similar yarn.

As package sizes increased, labour costs in doffing, handling and rewinding fell, and gave the ring frame further economic advantage over the mule: it already had the considerable advantage that it could be tended by women. However, the quality advantage of the mule remained, and in countries which had to import their cotton, the ability of the mule to spin a better yarn from a given quality of cotton delayed the adoption of the ring frame. For many years this was an important consideration in Europe, but as the price of cotton continued to fall in relation to labour costs it became of less importance. Meanwhile, developments in the technology of roller drafting were slowly but surely removing the need for any drafting-against-twist. In 1780 this feature of the mule-spinning process enabled Crompton to spin yarns incomparably superior to the purely roller-drafted yarns of the water frames. Considerable progress was made in roller drafting during the nineteenth century, but the advantage of the mule remained real until well into the present century.

A most decisive contribution to drafting was made by Fernando Casablancas, who introduced the now familiar double-apron drafting system in Spain in 1914. It was not a new concept, apron-drafting systems of one sort or another having been experimented with for almost a century, but the Casablancas system was the first to achieve wide acceptance. The great claim of Casablancas was for 'high' (in America 'long') drafts. The three-roller system on ring frames was limited to overall draft ratios in the range 7 to 10, depending on the cotton and the count: but appreciably higher overall ratios could be used on mules because of the levelling effect of the carriage draft. Initially the Casablancas system could be used on ring frames for ratios up to about 20 with the advantage that it gave satisfactory levelness without carriage draft.

Considerable interest arose in the further development of drafting technology, and between 1935 and 1950 the fundamentals of roller and apron drafting were the subject of much painstaking research, in particular by G. A. R. Foster of the Shirley Institute, Manchester. The outcome was a body of knowledge which, when applied to the design and operation of practical drafting systems, transformed the situation. The number of preparatory drafting processes required before spinning was halved, typically from six to three, and at the same time both the uniformity and the strength of the yarns were greatly increased. The present situation is that all yarns of commercial importance, from the coarsest to the finest, from the softest to the hardest, can be spun on ring frames. Over the whole range, modern ring-spun yarns are more uniform than were comparable mule-spun yarns and, from the same cottons and with the same twist factors, from 15 to 40 per cent stronger. In addition ring frames are cheap (1968 price c £12 per spindle) and compact. They produce yarn at roughly twice the hourly rate of existing mules and, being simple and non-temperamental, are suitable for multi-shift working.

In view of these facts it is not surprising that the mule is now virtually obsolete. Its disappearance from the scene has been slow but very few now remain. Replacement of mules by rings took place very early in America, the birthplace of the ring frame, and by 1939 rather less than 1 per cent of the 27,000,000 spindles then in use in North America were mule spindles. These few remnants did not survive for many years and few people now in the American industry have ever seen a mule outside a museum. Mules survived longer in Europe, particularly in Britain. In 1939 the total number of spindles in Europe (excluding Britain) was 42,300,000 of which roughly one-quarter were mule spindles. By 1951 the proportion had fallen to only 6 per cent and few now remain.

The picture of decline in Britain is greatly complicated by the fact that for the first quarter of the present century cotton textiles were a large and extremely important export. During that period it was said that all the requirements of the home trade were met before breakfast, and the remainder of the working day was devoted to goods for export. This was quite literally true, for only about one-tenth of the yarn spun in Lancashire was retained, the rest being exported either as yarn or in cloth. In 1907, of 7,000,000,000 yd of cloth manufactured in Britain, 6,300,000,000 yd were exported as piece goods. In addition, a substantial amount of yarn was exported and more cloth was exported in the form of made-up garments. At that time Britain had more than one-third of the total number of spindles in the world and more than 80 per cent of them were mule spindles.

Slowly at first, both the total number of spindles and the proportion of mule spindles declined. In response to the short-lived post-war boom of the 1920s, the total number of spindles in Britain reached an all-time peak in 1927 of 60,465,000, of which 46,851,000 (c 78 per cent) were mule spindles. In the succeeding depression many mills were closed for ever and the total number of spindles fell dramatically to 36,322,000 by 1939, the growth of sixty years having been lost in little more than a decade. During this contraction, casualties were rather higher amongst mule-equipped companies spinning the finer counts, and at the start of World War II the proportion of mule spindles had fallen to roughly 70 per cent of the total.

During the war, clothes rationing and disruption of the export trade greatly restricted textile activity in Britain and the industry was concentrated under strict Government control. In the years immediately after the war textile markets throughout the world were exceptionally buoyant. As part of the national fiscal policy the industry was re-expanded to make a maximum contribution to exports. Only essential re-equipment was undertaken during this period, as the textile-machinery industry was fully engaged in meeting the abnormal world demand for its products. When the post-war boom ended (c 1951) the British industry had a total of 28,252,000 spindles, of which 17,905,000 (c 64 per cent) were mule spindles.

By this time most of the mules were more than forty years old and many of the ring frames were also due for renewal. Mills throughout Britain began to re-equip and rationalise their activities to meet the changed world situation. Mules, for the first time, played no part. One Oldham company had sufficient confidence in the inherent superiority of the mule to place an order for a complete new installation of about 80,000 spindles: had this venture succeeded perhaps others would have followed, but it failed. The machinery maker brought his specification up-to-date in the engineering sense and attempted to meet the order. Six mules were eventually delivered but considerable difficulties arose from the fact that twenty-five years had elapsed since the last order for mules had been executed. The new mules did not run as well as the old ones they were intended to replace, and in the end the old mules were reconditioned as a compromise solution.

This was decisively the end of the road. No new mules have since been built and almost all those then existing have been scrapped. After the collapse of the boom in 1951 mills again began to close, and although many more spindles were scrapped the industry was clearly too large for our needs. Realising this, the British Government in 1959 introduced an Act to bring about the contraction and reorganisation of the cotton industry by subsidising the scrapping of obsolete machinery and assisting re-equipment of the mills electing to remain in the industry. At the time of the Act roughly 20,000,000 spindles remained in the industry and almost half of them were scrapped under its provisions. Of the few mule spindles left almost all were scrapped in the succeeding wave of mergers and mill closures. There are now (1969) fewer than 4,000,000 cotton spinning spindles of all types in Britain and less than 300,000 of these are mule spindles.

To put the present size of the industry into perspective, however, it is important to appreciate that these 4,000,000 spindles are almost all on modern high-speed ring frames, which spin at about twice the speed of mules and are operated very intensively for up to 160 hours a week. Thus the present productive capacity of the industry is roughly equal to that of an industry of 30,000,000 mule spindles working day-shifts only in the traditional way.

It is proper to mourn the passing of the mule, but it must be admitted that the economic superiority of the ring frame has made it inevitable. In the 1820s, when the hand mule was almost the universal spinning machine, a labour force of 125,000 people produced 130,000,000 lb of yarn annually—rather more than 1,000 lb per operative per year. Productivity rose steadily with the introduction and perfection of the self-actor to a maximum of 8,400 lb per operative per year in 1913. Thereafter it fell to 6,700 lb per operative per year in the 1920s. As the proportion of ring frames became appreciable, productivity began to rise again, passing the 1913 figure in the early 1950s and reaching a new peak of 14,800 lb per operative in the year 1969.

Spinning technology is still advancing. Already the ring frame itself is being challenged by a new machine which is able to spin extremely regular yarns at speeds in the order of 50,000 rpm. It is clear that there is no place in the industry of the future for Crompton's great invention. Like the crossbow, the stagecoach and the square-rigged clipper ship, the mule burst upon an astonished world, had its brief hour of glory and is now eclipsed. To coming generations it may seem incredible that such a machine, with a carriage 150 ft long and carrying 1,300 spindles in a single row, could ever have been built. It will seem even less credible that in Lancashire alone there were once nearly 50,000,000 mule spindles, each accelerated to 10,000 rpm before being stopped and reversed with infinite precision four times a minute throughout a fifty-six hour week. Soon there will be only a few drastically shortened remnants of this great army of awe-inspiring machines standing lifeless in our museums to remind us of what has been.

Glossary

Backing-off. Operation performed on completion of a draw, in which the spindles are turned backwards to unwind the coils of yarn from the spindle blade.

Balloon. The whirling yarn between the rollers and the traveller in the ring-spinning process.

Binding coils. The few very oblique coils of yarn wound onto the cop chase at the beginning of each run-in. The purpose of these coils is to give the cop mechanical strength.

Boot leg. A pendent lever which controls the position of the faller during winding.

Bosses. The individual leather-covered rollers which run in contact with the fluted steel drafting rollers.

Break draft. A low degree of attenuation of a roving, just sufficient to draw-out the twist, applied prior to the main draft in a multi-zone drafting system.

Cap frame. A form of continuous spinning machine, historically coming between the throstle and the ring frame. It is still used for worsted spinning.

Card. A fine but stiff wire brush by means of which fibrous materials may be disentangled preparatory to spinning. The term is also used as a verb. In addition it is loosely applied to mean a carding engine, ie a machine by which cotton, wool, jute or flax is disentangled and formed into a sliver (or into rovings in the case of a card fitted with a condenser).

Card web. The almost transparent film of fibres produced by a carding engine.

Carriage. The carriage supporting the spindles and permitting them to be moved away from or towards the rollers.

Catch box. A toothed clutch normally held in engagement by a spring or a weighted lever.

Comber. A machine which combs out all short fibre from cotton or wool stock.

Condenser system. A system of spinning in which fibres are condensed to form rovings directly they leave the card. The rovings are then twisted to form yarn with virtually no drafting. The result is a soft, full yarn in which there is a great deal of entanglement of the fibres.

Cones or cheeses. Large bobbins of yarn, respectively conical or cylindrical.

Cop. A cylindrical yarn package with conical ends, so constructed that the yarn may be withdrawn substantially axially from one of the conical ends without rotation of the package.

Cop body. The cylindrical part of a cop.

Cop bottom. That part of a cop which is formed up to the point of reaching the body diameter.

Cop chase. The upper cone of a cop. That part of the cop surface onto which yarn is wound during the formation of the cop.

Copping rail. A linear cam used to control the guiding of the yarn during winding.

Count. Number describing the fineness of the yarn. For cotton yarns the count is the number of hanks, each of 840 yd, in 1 lb of yarn.

Counterfaller. Device to take up the slack, and thereby maintain approximately constant tension, in the yarn during winding.

Countershaft. A lay shaft. On self-acting mules it is usually arranged parallel to, and mounted directly above, the rim shaft.

Creel. Frame supporting the bobbins of roving. To renew bobbins of roving as they become exhausted.

Crow. An Oldham stick.

Doff. To remove completed cops from the spindles.

Drafting. The drawing-out of slivers, slubbings or rovings to straighten and parallelise the fibres. The effect of this is to produce a lean, strong yarn of high lustre.

Drafting rollers. Arrangement of rollers by which the primary attenuation of the roving is performed.

Draw. That part of the mule cycle of operations during which the spindles are withdrawn from the rollers and secondary attenuation takes place, accompanied by twist insertion.

Draw bands. Ropes attached to helically-grooved drums on the backshaft and used to control movement of the carriage during the draw.

End. A continuous length of yarn.

Faller. Device to guide the yarn onto the cop chase during winding.

Faller wire. Part of the faller. A taut wire, extending the length of the mule, which actually contacts the yarn during winding.

Finishing. The processes through which cloth passes after weaving. Scouring, bleaching, dyeing and printing are all finishing processes.

Fluker rod. A rotating metal rod mounted below the drafting rollers in such a position that it picks up the untwisted roving issuing from the drafting rollers when an end is broken. Used only on Bolton-style mules.

Fly. The rim. Also short or broken fibre released during processing.

Flyer. The rotating arm of a Saxony wheel, both when used for spinning and also when used for the preparation of rovings.

Get-up. To piece up (or repair) broken ends. In some districts 'gait-up'.

Governing motion. A strapping motion.

Hank. Unit of length: of cotton 840 yd, of worsted 560 yd.

Headstock. The major assembly of mechanical components by means of which the working elements of a mule are controlled.

High draft. The very high attenuation ratio possible with the highly developed drafting systems which have become available in relatively recent times.

Jacking. The drawing out of a partially twisted yarn in order to get greater uniformity.

Jenny. A machine on which yarn is made by a discontinuous process in which drafting against twist while spinning is followed by winding the yarn thus made onto the spindle used for spinning.

Jennygate. The part of a spinning room traversed by the mule carriage.

Laying-on. Reverse process to backing-off. Performed on completion of winding and is the formation of the spindle-blade coils for the imminent draw.

Let-in (or light-in). The arrival of the mule carriage at the end of the inward run.

Long Lever. A rocking lever mounted on the side of a mule head-stock.

Mule. A mule jenny.

Mule jenny. A hybrid machine combining the drafting-against-twist discontinuous process of the jenny and the system of roller drafting used in the water frame. Later, a manually controlled mule as distinct from the self-actor.

Nicking (or necking). The partial severance of a spun yarn.

Nip. The point at which a pair of rollers may be regarded as gripping a roving or yarn.

Nosing motion. A device providing supplementary acceleration of the spindles when winding on the apex of the cop chase during the later stages of cop formation.

Nosing peg. A peg which is carried by the quadrant and which, by deflecting the winding chain, acts as a nosing motion.

Pair. Loosely used to mean a pair of mules.

Picking the sticks. Removing, cleaning and replacing the sticks on Oldham-style mules.

Pirns. Yarn packages specially suited to the shuttles of automatic (pirn changing) looms.

Put-up. To drive the mule carriage inwards while controlling the winding process. Although applicable to self-actors it is a term more generally applied to the manual operation of mule jennies.

Quadrant. An important element of the mechanism used to rotate the spindles during winding.

Quadrant bands. Ropes arranged to relate the angular movement of the quadrant to the linear movement of the carriage.

Quadrant nut. The point of attachment of the winding chain to the quadrant.

Quadrant screw. The screw by means of which the radial position of the quadrant nut is controlled.

Ratch. The difference between carriage speed and roller-delivery speed on a condenser or woollen mule.

Rim. A large pulley (usually multi-grooved) used to drive the spindles during the draw.

Rim band. An endless driving band by means of which the tin roller is driven from the rim.

Rim shaft. The main shaft of a mule to which is attached the rim.

Ring frame. A continuous spinning machine which has largely displaced mules.

Roller lap. A layer of roving or yarn wound tightly round a drafting roller as a result of breakage or other malfunction.

Roving. A thin rope of lightly twisted, substantially parallel fibres from which yarn is spun.

Sawney. A simultaneous breakage of all the ends of yarn on a spinning machine.

Scroll bands. Heavy ropes, each having one end attached to the carriage and the other end wrapped round and secured to a scroll. The check scroll bands also pass round fixed pulleys at the front of the headstock so that they may retard the carriage at the end of the inward run.

Scrolls. Spirally grooved drums used to control the motion of the mule carriage during the inward run.

Self-actor. A completely automatic mule.

Set. All the cops made at one time on a mule.

Short rail. A type of copping rail used on Bolton-style mules. So called because it is only about one-third of the length of the more usual type of copping rail.

Slip. One of the rails on which the carriage runs. Loosely used to mean part of the mulegate between adjacent slips.

Sliver. A thick, soft, untwisted rope of fibre.

Slub. A thick untwisted group of fibres forming a fault in a yarn.

Slubbing. A lightly twisted rope of fibre roughly intermediate between a sliver and a roving.

Snarl. A twisted entanglement which results when a newly twisted yarn is allowed to go slack.

Spindle band. A light endless cord by means of which a spindle is driven from the tin roller.

Spindle blade. The upper part of a spindle on which the cop is formed.

Squaring bands. Ropes so arranged that they keep the mule carriage 'square'—ie parallel to the rollers, at all times.

Stang. A general term for a handle. Applied particularly to the handle by which the strap fork mechanism controlling the main drive to a mule was operated.

Sticks. The underclearers.

Strapping band. The band of rope by which motion is transmitted from the carriage to the quadrant screw.

Strapping motion. A device for automatically re-setting the quadrant nut during cop bottom formation.

Taking-up. The drawing-in of the mule carriage.

Throstle. A continuous spinning machine developed from the water frame.

Thrutching-up. The loosening and partial lifting of all the cops on a mule prior to doffing.

Tin roller. A cylinder extending the whole length of the carriage which when rotated drives the spindles by means of individual spindle bands.

Twist. Yarn intended for use as warp. Helical distortion of the fibres forming a yarn.

Twist factor. Factor relating the number of turns of twist per unit length to the count of a yarn.

Underclearers. Flannel-covered rollers which run in contact with the fluted steel delivery roller of the drafting system. They serve the dual purpose of keeping the roller clean and picking up untwisted roving when an end is broken. Not used on Bolton-style mules.

Unlocking bracket. A member fixed to the headstock for disengaging the faller from the control of the copping rail on completion of winding.

Water frame. A continuous spinning machine combining the twisting principle of the Saxony wheel with roller draft. No water is used in the machine itself. The name was given merely because the early machines were driven from a waterwheel.

Weft. Yarn intended for the shuttle of a loom. The term is sometimes loosely used to mean yarn spun on mules whether for warp or for weft.

Whorl. A small disc or pulley secured to a spindle.

Winding. That part of the cycle of operations in which the yarn spun during a draw is wound onto the spindle in the form of a cop.

Winding block. A cylindrical drum mounted on the carriage and mechanically coupled to the tin roller during winding.

Winding chain. A strong chain having one end attached to the quadrant and the other end wound round and secured to the winding block.

Winding faller. The faller.

Woollen. A woollen yarn is a soft full yarn prepared and spun on the condenser system.

Worsted. A worsted yarn is a lean strong yarn made from wool which has been combed and drafted.

Yarn. Spun thread.

Yarn sheet. All the yarn between the spindles and the rollers.

Museums of Textile History

A selection of sites in the North of England where material relevant to the history of the spinning mule may be seen.

Blackburn	Lewis Textile Museum, Exchange Street, Blackburn, Lancashire *Tel. (02540) 667130*
Bolton	Central Museum & Art Gallery, Le Mans Crescent, Bolton, Lancashire B11 1SE *Tel. (0204) 22311 Ext. 379* Tonge Moor Textile Museum, Tonge Moor Library, Tonge Moor Road, Bolton, Lancashire *Tel. (0204) 21394/22311 Ext. 383* Hall i'th' Wood, Green Way, off Crompton Way, Bolton, Lancashire BL1 8UA *Tel. (0204) 51159*
Bradford	Bradford Industrial Museum, Moorside Road, Eccleshill, Bradford BD2 3HP *Tel. (0274) 631756*
Halifax	Calderdale Industrial Museum, Central Works, Square Road, Halifax *Tel. (0422) 59031*
Helmshore	Museum of the Lancashire Textile Industry, Higher Mill, Holcombe Road, Helmshore, Rossendale, Lancashire BB4 4NP *Tel. (0706) 226459*
Leeds	Leeds Industrial Museum, Armley Mills, Canal Road, Armley, Leeds *Tel. (0532) 637862*
Manchester	Greater Manchester Museum of Science and Industry, Liverpool Road Station, Liverpool Road, Castlefield, Manchester M3 4JP *Tel. (061) 832 2244*
Oldham	Local Interest Centre, Greaves Street, Oldham *Tel. (061) 6784654*
Saddleworth	Saddleworth Museum and Art Gallery, High Street, Uppermill, Oldham OL3 6HS *Tel. (045) 774093*
Styal	Quarry Bank Mill, Styal, Cheshire SK9 4LA *Tel. (0625) 527468*

Bibliography

Aspin, C. *James Hargreaves and the Spinning Jenny* (Guardian Press, 1964)

Baines, Edward. *History of the Cotton Manufacture in Great Britain.* (Fisher, Fisher & Jackson, 1835)

Cameron, H. C. *Samuel Crompton* (Blatchworth Press, 1951)

Catling, H. & De Barr, A. E. 'The Profile of Cop Build Ring Bobbins', *Proceedings of the Textile Institute* (1958), Vol 50, pp 385–9

Catling, H. 'Kinematics of Control of the Winding Process in the Spinning Mule' (University of London Ph D thesis, 1965)

Chapman, Sydney. *The Lancashire Cotton Industry* (Sherratt & Hughes, 1904)

Committee on Industry and Trade. *Survey of Textile Industries* (HMSO, 1928)

Derry, T. K. & Williams, T. I. *A Short History of Technology* (Oxford University Press, 1960)

Dobson, B. P. *The Evolution of the Spinning Machine* (Marsden, 1910)

French, Gilbert J. *Life and Times of Samuel Crompton* (Simpkin, Marshall, 1859)

Guest, Richard. *Compendious History of the Cotton Manufacture* (Pratts, 1823)[1]

Kelly, William. Patent Specification of 14th May in the 32nd Year of the Reign of King George the Third (1792)

Kennedy, John. 'Rise and Progress of the Cotton Trade', *Memoirs*

[1] Full title is A compendious history of the Cotton Manufacture with a disproval of the claim of Sir Richard Arkwright to the invention of its ingenious machinery.

of the Manchester Literary & Philosophic Society (1819 vol 3, 115–137)[2]

Leigh, Evan. *Modern Cotton Spinning* (Palmer & Howe, 1877)

Marsden, Richard. *Cotton Spinning* (George Bell, 1884)

McConnell, John. *Century of Fine Cotton Spinning* (George Faulkener, 1906)

Montgomery, James. *Theory and Practice of Cotton Spinning* (John Niven, 1836)

Murphy, William S. *The Textile Industries* (Gresham, 1910)

Nasmith, Joseph. *Principles and Construction of Cotton Spinning Machinery* (John Heywood, 1890)

Nasmith, Joseph. *The Student's Cotton Spinning* (John Heywood, 1896)

Neste, Kurt. *The Mule Spinning Process* (John Heywood, 1865)

Paul, Lewis. Patent Specification. Twentieth part of Close Rolls in the Twelfth Year of King George the Second (1738)

Platt, John. 'Machinery for the Preparing and Spinning of Cotton', *Proceedings of the Institution of Mechanical Engineers* (1886) pp 199–244

Roberts, Richard. Patent Specification No 5949 of 1 July 1830

Scott-Taggart, William. 'The Quadrant and Shaper of the Self-acting Mule', (Bolton & District Managers & Overlookers Association, 1898)

Scott-Taggart, William. *Cotton Spinning* (Macmillan, 1907)

Spencer, Eli. 'Improvements in Machinery for Preparing and Spinning Cotton', *Proceedings of the Institution of Mechanical Engineers* (1880) pp 492–528

Thornley, Thomas. *Self-acting Mules* (John Heywood, 1893)

Thornley, Thomas. *Mule Spinning* (John Heywood, 1899)

Wood, L. S. & Wilmore, A. *The Cotton Industry in England* (Oxford University Press, 1927)

[2] Full title is Observations on the Rise and Progress of the Cotton Trade in Gt Britain particularly in Lancashire and the adjoining counties.

Index

INDEX

Helmshore

Museum of the LANCASHIRE TEXTILE INDUSTRY

The decline in the commercial use of the mule has continued since the first edition of the "Spinning Mule" was published in 1970. Just one Lancashire Mill remains where mules are still in commercial use. There are a number of museums where mules can be seen, but only one or two locations show workable full length examples. Only at Helmshore Museum can 714 spindle Taylor Lang mules be seen working in the setting they have occupied for over fifty years.

Helmshore Museum has recently acquired an Asa Lees medium count cotton spinning mule which is 132 ft (39.5m) long. This is believed to be the only surviving example of a medium or fine count cotton mule which has not been drastically shortened in length. Restoration work is in progress and it is hoped to erect and operate this machine in the not too distant future.

Museum of the Lancashire Textile Industry, Higher Mill,
Holcombe Road, Helmshore, Rossendale, Lancashire BB4 4NP.
Telephone Rossendale (0706) 226459